WOODY ALLEN'S
PLAY IT AGAIN, SAM

WOODY ALLEN'S
PLAY IT AGAIN, SAM

EDITED BY
RICHARD J. ANOBILE

GROSSET & DUNLAP
A FILMWAYS COMPANY
Publishers • New York

ABOUT THE AUTHOR

RICHARD J. ANOBILE is considered to be the most consistently successful producer of film related books. Since 1969 he has had eighteen books published, all of which have been critically acclaimed as the best of their genre.

Anobile studied motion picture direction and production at the City University of New York's Institute of Film Technique.

Although an inveterate New Yorker, Anobile now lives in Hollywood where he is developing various feature film projects. He hopes to produce while continuing his work on several new book projects.

INTRODUCTION

On screen a debonair man deftly woos a sophisticated woman. Watching that screen, a sad-eyed young man attempts to show his sweetheart that he loves her.

The young man fumbles for a while, but try as he may, he still can't seem to overcome being shy. Then, taking his cue from the obviously seasoned screen lover, Buster Keaton finally musters the courage to kiss the woman he has wanted from the outset of reel one. That was 1924. The film is *Sherlock Jr.*

Forty-eight years later another young man searches the screen looking for that same confidence. Woody Allen latches on to Bogart, his ultimate fantasy of the perfect lover, who provides him with the courage to begin being himself. The film is *Play It Again, Sam.*

Since their beginning, the movies have subtly played a role in forming our concepts of what we should be; of our outward mannerisms, modes of speech, and dress. The pendulum, of film reflecting life and reality reflecting celluloid fantasy, seems to be in perpetual motion. A persuasive case can be argued either way, but ultimately it is a chicken-or-egg disagreement.

Play It Again, Sam has always seemed to me a logical beginning for a look at the film output of Woody Allen. It is the calling card of his true promise as a comic filmmaker.

Although by 1972 Allen had already directed two features, *Bananas* and *Take the Money and Run,* he had yet to become an accomplished enough filmmaker to realize the full potential of the material in *Play It Again, Sam.* That Allen allowed another director to give the piece the shape it would need for the screen is to his credit.

Play It Again, Sam is a marvelously funny film. You don't need me or anyone else to tell you that. The director, Herbert Ross, and screenwriter Allen have structured a comic film that is perfectly balanced in the use of visual gags and verbal witticism. As entertainment, the film ranks with the cinema's finest achievements. But *Play It Again, Sam* is much more than this.

Allen's own films have tended to be collections of loosely structured comic vignettes. And despite glimpses of superlative scripting and inventive direction, Allen's films since 1972 never seemed to fulfill the promise of *Play It Again, Sam.*

But with *Annie Hall* (1977) that seems to have changed. This new film is by far Allen's most masterful work and thrusts him to the forefront of American com-

ic filmmakers. In a sense it continues the promise of *Play It Again, Sam* and could easily be considered its sequel.

Whether he is performing in nightclubs, on television, or in film, Woody Allen always preys upon his own insecurities for material. His public persona might be more autobiographical than anyone suspects.

Allen's continued success with one basic theme is evidence that he has struck the mother lode of a universal truth. Though some critics have found Allen's image of insecurity increasingly tedious, audiences are still attuned to his material.

We laugh with Allen because many of our own insecurities are pictured up on that screen. We laugh to ease the tension of revelation and run for cover from the place where we have unexpectedly become vulnerable. Though the process is veiled in the guise of entertainment, a nerve has been struck. Allen exposes that which we are ever careful to shield from the view of others but about which we are constantly aware.

Thinking about living a fantasy has always been easier and seemingly more fun than dealing with reality. Unfortunately, fantasies are usually not what they are cracked up to be. Reality just doesn't perform according to our programming. As we grow older we tend to be better able to separate fantasy and reality. We understand that one cannot exist in both worlds and come out whole. And for most of us fantasy remains within ourselves as a healthy accouterment to reality.

For Allan Felix, the main character in *Play It Again, Sam,* Bogart represents the quintessence of the man for whom women search. Bogart is cool. He knows exactly what to say, how to say it, and when. He's tough yet soft. And the women in Bogart's world always want him. But as is readily apparent, that concept of Bogart is different from the actual Bogart's screen character. It is a fantasy in itself. Only the form resembles Bogart.

Allan's (the character's) creation is a shell devoid of feelings. There is no soul. The fantasy Bogart speaks and acts like the real thing, but the cliché-ridden Bogart dialogue sounds silly and out of place, even to Allan, who nevertheless uses it and clings to it as he once clung to his mother's breast. It is not until Bogart is unexpectedly whisked from the scene by a castration-fantasy gun moll—in the form of Allan's ex-wife—that Allan must make do on his own.

Despite the comedic lunge Allan makes in finally telling

Linda that he loves her, and despite his second thoughts, his feelings ring true. As clumsy as the attempt was, he has taken a step forward. The realization that Allan has been limiting himself sets in. He moves closer to being himself.

Growing up in the age of movies and television has had a numbing effect upon our concept of self. It is one thing to read about a hero or heroine—or just hear him or her, as was the case with radio. It is quite another thing altogether to be presented with a *fait accompli*: the total embodiment of the role. Instead of picturing ourselves in the role, we picture a particular actor. We are taught automatically to exclude ourselves, the ultimate of the very rejection we struggle to avoid.

Further, we isolate ourselves from others who do not fulfill the images of men and women fed us via the screen. Only lately have we begun to sense that "larger than life" is not necessarily good.

The infringement of media upon each of us is likely to continue and increase as more and more technological advances push into our homes and vie with the outside world for our attention. Only an interest in self will allow us to keep in proper perspective, the media and the bigger-than-life fantasies they seem to create.

It is such perspective that prevails in *Play It Again, Sam*. As Allan Felix sees that it is actually his own personality that has attracted Linda, he has no choice but to begin discarding the Bogart caricature he has created. It is difficult to pinpoint the mechanics of the winning confrontation in Allan's mind. But it would seem to occur at the moment he routinely utters those famous *Casablanca* lines to Linda during a real situation: "If that plane leaves the ground and you're not with him, you'll regret it. Maybe not today, maybe not tomorrow, but soon, and for the rest of your life." Linda tells Allan that what he just said was beautiful. In a flash, Allan confesses that the lines are from *Casablanca*. And although the balance of the scene is played out according to the script, it is now almost matter-of-factly running its course. Reality has encroached upon fantasy and demands recognition.

And to make it even clearer, the final frames of *Casablanca* are duplicated only to a point. Recall that in the original Bogart walks off with Claude Rains to the words, "Louis, I think this is the beginning of a beautiful friendship." When Allan Felix walks into the fog, he is alone. His Bogart creation has been left behind, bidding him adieu.

Richard J. Anobile
Hollywood, California
March 1977

ABOUT HERBERT ROSS

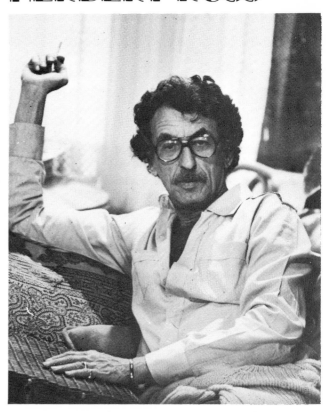

Up until the time Mr. Ross directed *Play It Again, Sam,* his film credits included Natalie Wood's dance number in *Inside Daisy Clover,* the set pieces for Otto Preminger's *Carmen Jones,* and Rex Harrison's numbers in *Dr. Dolittle*. He had directed *Goodbye, Mr. Chips,* starring Peter O'Toole, and *The Owl and the Pussycat,* starring Barbra Streisand. Since then his films as director have included *T. R. Baskin, Funny Lady, The Last of Sheila, The Sunshine Boys,* and *The Seven-Per-Cent Solution*.

Herbert Ross began his career in dance. As a choreographer he staged musical numbers for many Broadway shows, including *A Tree Grows in Brooklyn* and *I Can Get It for You Wholesale*. For ballet Mr. Ross created *Caprichos,* inspired by Goya, and *The Maids* based on Jean Genet's play. The two works remain in the repertory of the American Ballet Theatre.

At the time of my interview with him, Mr. Ross was completing work on *The Turning Point* for 20th Century–Fox, a film starring Anne Bancroft, Shirley MacLaine, and Mikhail Baryshnikov. The film blends Mr. Ross's talent for filmmaking with his love of ballet. And while *The Turning Point* was in post production Mr. Ross began directing *The Goodbye Girl* for Warner Bros. That film has a script by Neil Simon and stars Richard Dreyfuss and Marsha Mason.

Mr. Ross has described his approach to filmmaking as follows: "I appreciate human values. I admire speech which is bright and informed and witty and educated. I don't think that has gone out of fashion. You can have *Trader Horn* and *King Kong* too, but there was always an audience for Hepburn and Tracy and for Astaire and Rogers.

"I really hate to repeat myself. The easiest thing in the world, especially if you have a hit early on, is to go on making the same film over and over. Some directors have made a career of it, which is perfectly all right. It just isn't for me. The only fun of success for me—once you realize that you don't get to keep much of the money—is the freedom it buys you. The freedom to try something else next time.

"I like thrillers. I'd like to do a western. I'd like to do a spectacle, but it would be more Mike Todd than Cecil B. de Mille. If there is a pattern to the eclectic films I do, it is that they all point toward affirmation, that there are enduring values by which our lives are best led, and that our culture, our art, our lives are all part of the civilization which is what our life is all about."

The following interview took place on March 18, 1977, at the MGM Studios in Culver City on the set of *The Goodbye Girl*.

WITH HERBERT ROSS

ANOBILE: *Play It Again, Sam* began as a stage play on Broadway. How did you become involved with it when it was decided that the play would be made into a film?

ROSS: Well, Arthur P. Jacobs, who produced the film, had bought the rights to the play prior to its opening on Broadway. After the show closed Jacobs had planned to produce the film for 20th Century–Fox, which already had $600,000 into the project. But for some reason Fox declined and Jacobs brought the project to Paramount Pictures while Robert Evans was head of production. Paramount bought out Fox—at a very good buy I might add—and that's how the picture got started. I believe that I was Arthur's first choice for a director. I had never seen the play, so I read it and then met Woody. Well, I asked Woody why he didn't want to direct it and he mentioned that he felt that as a play it was too structured and therefore he didn't direct it for the stage. He wanted it that way for the film.

ANOBILE: Yet he would be writing the screenplay.

ROSS: That's right. And when he sent me the first draft, it was the play which he had marked with things like, "Exterior—Allan crosses stage left!" He hadn't bothered rewriting it.

So I called him up and told him that I thought I knew how the script could be written without changing any of the text. And I made some suggestions as to where I felt the action could take place and so forth. It was my idea to do the Bogart/*Casablanca* opening. Woody liked that.

ANOBILE: How had that concept been set up onstage?

ROSS: Simply through a monologue. And in his original screen draft Woody hadn't done anything to adapt that monologue for the film.

You see, in Woody's own films, those that he directs, he does do monologues. He addresses an unseen audience or will address you directly. And he uses a great deal of voice-over. It's a personal technique.

ANOBILE: Then, would the final version of the script be more aptly described as a collaboration between Allen and yourself or was what you added a function of your direction in that you were showing him what could be more visual?

ROSS: The latter is exactly right. I asked him to write several new scenes in instances where I felt the characters should be moving from one place to another. I was looking for a shape for the picture and that's how I started looking at the old Bogart films.

From that came the opening sequence under the titles and the idea to paraphrase the last sequence of *Casablanca* shot by shot. I wanted to have that last scene in our picture play in the same style as the last scene in *Casablanca*. I wanted Woody, Diane Keaton, and Tony Roberts to play that scene as honestly as Bogart, Bergman, and Henreid had played it.

ANOBILE: And it works. I have done a reconstruction of *Casablanca* and no matter how corny one may think the film is, especially viewing it from a seventies perspective, that sequence is nevertheless very affecting. And in running your film for this book, especially going through your last reel, I found myself feeling the same emotional tug that I had felt when viewing *Casablanca*. Something about that scene is basic. It's structured so that the viewer is literally pulled into it emotionally.

ROSS: It's a wonderfully written scene. It's about something everybody understands—renunciation. About doing it well, about behaving well under stress. Grace under pressure! Anyway, after having made various choices and having Woody rewrite some scenes, the picture was ready to shoot on location in New York. But within two weeks of our start date there was a film strike in New York. It meant canceling the shoot.

I refused to make the picture in Los Angeles because it was the wrong atmosphere for the story. So I suggested San Francisco. Woody agreed but was a bit nervous about it. But San Francisco did have all the elements the story required—a university life, a film culture, and beaches.

Well, we went to San Francisco and found all the locations a week before we were to begin rehearsals. Everything was shot on location. Allan's apartment was actually the home of a young man who was an amateur filmmaker and a local film critic. And the beach house belonged to people who were in the class equivalent to the people Diane and Tony portrayed in the film.

ANOBILE: By the time you began to work on *Play It Again, Sam*, Woody Allen had already directed two features, *Bananas* and *Take the Money and Run*. Given this, did you have any problem directing someone who had now become accustomed to directing himself?

ROSS: No. Woody is terribly open and modest. And we are very good friends still. We used to view the dailies together and I'd rely on his judgment at times. Sometimes I'd agree and other times I'd disagree with him, but I enjoyed going over the dailies with him. There was an adjustment that he and Tony Roberts had to make in that they had done the play. It was an adjustment in tone, which in the movie is far more refined. The play was broader and cruder. When we began rehearsals I suggested that we forget that we were doing a comedy. I wanted it to be funny, but played more for the play. For example, Tony's character could have ended up a mere caricature if it had been taken too far.

All in all, the entire project went very smoothly and I think we shot the picture in forty days, maybe less. We did just about everything ourselves and just set out to make a movie. And it was always a movie in everyone's mind, not an adaptation.

ANOBILE: Of all the Woody Allen films thus far—I haven't yet seen *Annie Hall*—*Play It Again, Sam* is his most structured, storywise, and in a sense the most cinematic in that it flows well from most aspects.

ROSS: I believe that Woody is very proud of the film. He did tell me that he learned a great deal from watching it come together. I do think that the nature of his own work shifted slightly after this film and his technique began to be a bit more sophisticated.

Certainly *Love* and *Death* is an attempt to make a movie, as opposed to a series of photographed sketches. Prior to shooting our film I had seen only *Bananas*.

ANOBILE: I would imagine that *Bananas* could have led you to anticipate having some problems with Allen.

ROSS: Yes, that's right. It made me nervous. I thought that the film had some wonderfully funny things in it but it made me edgy.

Yet, when I finally met Woody, who is very educated and intelligent, and we began to talk, I didn't have any fears at all. I like his mind and the way he thinks. And I understood his humor.

The only time that we were a bit nervous during the project was the first day of shooting. We were doing the scene where he is introduced to Julie and he puts his hand in the salad. It was shot at The Trident Restaurant in San Francisco.

ANOBILE: That's where his ice cream pop goes up in the air.

ROSS: That's it! We shot thirty-seven takes on that scene alone.

Actually the first shot was that pan shot when Woody and Tony are walking through the restaurant having a conversation. Well, that went all right. But that little scene at the end of the sequence is what made us nervous because Woody couldn't get the piece of business right.

So, we shot it thirty-seven times and, by the way, ended up using the thirty-seventh take! Well, three days later I had a message back from Robert Evans

saying, "Do you think you will have to do as many takes for every scene?"

You see, I believe I had printed them all.

ANOBILE: In going over clippings from when the film was first released in 1972 I came across some criticism by women writers regarding the Allan character. Essentially the thrust of the criticism was that the writers were weary of seeing Woody Allen struggle to make out with women. It is a theme which runs through most of his films. How do you feel about this?

ROSS: That theme runs through *all* of his films. And as for *Play It Again, Sam,* it was the subject of the story. There is no plot without that story!

Now, I wouldn't want to do a film with that theme again, as I think Woody wrote it very well and said what there is to say about it. To do it again would have it become formula. But it is a classic theme. Chaplin had the same thing in every movie as well.

ANOBILE: I was struck by the great amounts of dialogue played over shots of characters moving from one place to another. I got a feeling that someone was constantly mindful that the play had to be opened up for the screen and hence a lot of walking and driving around.

ROSS: All those shots were my choices. You see, I knew that I had a very important scene to play in the third act of the piece. And a critical scene in the movie. That is where Allan tries to seduce Linda in his apartment.

I didn't want to use up my visual options before I got to that scene. And beyond that, the scenes to which you are referring are not dramatic scenes. I don't know how to explain them, but they are not rich in terms of drama.

ANOBILE: Essentially then, those scenes are there to provide the audience with information.

ROSS: Yes, they are, by nature, expository. I knew that I would have to play that apartment scene out. And if, for example, I situated one of those scenes you mentioned in a restaurant I'd be cutting back and forth and using up visual ideas I'd need to have for the scene I knew was coming.

ANOBILE: That seduction sequence is an interesting

Herbert Ross and Woody Allen

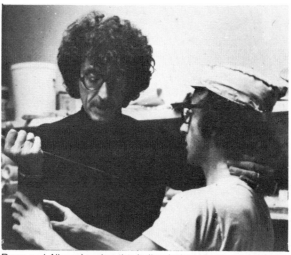

Ross and Allen planning the Italian bakery fantasy sequence.

The director and camera crew

and, in hindsight, a dangerously difficult scene to play within the context of the film.

Traditionally, a man who is attempting to seduce his best friend's wife is not a sympathetic character. While those mores have changed somewhat, nevertheless in the film the characters are in the more traditional situation. Up until that point the audience can easily sympathize with Allan.

How did you work out that scene to blunt what could have been rejection of the character by your audience?

ROSS: I think the difference is attitude. What we were playing, and I think the audience gets that, is that Allan's needs are greater than his friend's needs.

It has to do with priority. What Allan responds to is that for the first time a woman, because of her own particular problems, is interested in him. Her interest is the catalyst that ignites the flame which produces that response in him.

ANOBILE: There is a built-in crutch in that scene where Linda mentions that she is getting high on the champagne she is drinking. That seems as if it could be an excuse for what is happening.

ROSS: No, no. Actually, we were playing against that. Diane is not playing drunk. She's just using that as her excuse. What we also played is that Linda is the aggressor in that scene.

ANOBILE: How?

ROSS: Well, she could have gotten up and left. But what she was using—and this is a Victorian phrase—were women's wiles. She kept saying that she was drunk, but she never once said, "I want to leave because this has gone too far."

ANOBILE: So you are saying that she wanted those advances?

ROSS: Exactly that. Because of her own needs and her marital problems. She also had to feel needed.

It is a difficult scene but it just comes down to attitude. It is possible to play that scene really ugly! But that wasn't the tone of the piece. And it is not shirking to do it as we did. It is a matter of staying consistent with the writer's vision and style.

ANOBILE: In the scene Bogart coaches Allan through the seduction. At one point Allan finds Bogart's direction a bit schmaltzy. Yet Bogart persuades him and Allan feeds the line to Linda who responds positively. With that, Allan turns to Bogart, eyes wide open, and exclaims, "She bought it!" Now that is not a very charitable line for a character with whom the audience should be in sympathy!

ROSS: No. But Allan can't believe that this intelligent woman fell for this corny prom-date line.

Actually the moral issue is the same issue as the one in *Casablanca*. It is the very issue which makes the last scene in *Casablanca* work. In that film a married woman meets an old lover and they wish to be together. But eventually her sense of duty and honor compel her to remain with her husband. You know, "A far, far better think that I do." It's that kind of a code. That's true in *Play It Again, Sam* as well. That's the spine of the picture.

ANOBILE: In the last scene of your film Allan walks off with Bogart who is congratulating him for how he handled the situation with Linda. But it seems to boil down to merely a nice thing to do for another guy.

ROSS: No. I think he did what he did because he is whole. That's the point. You can't make a gesture like that unless you are complete.

Now, I'm talking very seriously. The experiences that Allan has had throughout the movie brought him to a point where he can perform an unselfish act. He's now able to give.

ANOBILE: So then the concept of the Bogart screen character is undercut. There is a disparity between Bogart and Allan, yet there is also a disparity between Bogart and what Allan thinks he is.

ROSS: Yes, because essentially what the movie is about, in a strange way, is outgrowing Bogart, outgrowing a childhood fantasy. And of course, the last shot is again a paraphrase of the last shot of Bogart and Claude Rains in *Casablanca*.

We shot that on a very windy night at the San Francisco airport. You can imagine what it was like to get that fog into the shot!

Ross and Allen on location at San Francisco's Trident Restaurant working on the scene which took thirty-seven takes to shoot.

In the apartment used as the home of Dick and Linda. L. to R.: Herbert Ross, Diane Keaton, Robert Evans and Woody Allen.

ABOUT THIS BOOK

For the past several years my books have dealt mainly with film classics. Of the eighteen books I have had published only one has presented a fairly contemporary film, *Psycho*. And even that film is now seventeen years in the past.

While it is healthy to recall the past and appreciate the groundwork laid by others who have come before us, it is also necessary to the vitality of the medium that we become aware of the classics being produced in our own time. Possibly it will stop us from lamenting that they do not produce films the way they used to in the old days. It will also be important to both future students of film and the general reader that we do not now re-create the mistakes of the past; that is, not adequately create reference materials during the lifetime of those who are making the film classics of tomorrow.

Although it is difficult to know now precisely what of today's film output will be considered classic many years hence, we can nevertheless apply basic standards of excellence to today's films and at least end up with more firsthand material than has been available to us previously. Couple that with material on films that for one reason or another have had a substantial impact upon the screen and its audience and we will at least be attempting to record the state of the art/industry as it occurs. Too much of what we know today about past filmmakers is based upon hearsay and critical assumptions. Our reference libraries are crammed with press releases as primary source material. Anyone minimally involved with film research will very quickly realize that the information in those releases is hardly worth the paper it is printed on.

Our concept of film has changed during the last twenty years. Therefore the reference materials we produce today must reflect our new attitude about an art that for too many years was just considered a business. The books we produce today should be as informative and factual as they are entertaining. We should not be passing on today's public relations myths to future readers except as an indication of where we were coming from.

I hope that this presentation of *Play It Again, Sam* will be the beginning of a new series of books presenting contemporary films for entertainment and reference. This represents a blend of my more popular film comedy series and the more esoteric Film Classics Library. I think this presentation will be of value to the more serious reader and at the same time will provide entertainment for those who want to have the film they once enjoyed on screen more readily available at home.

And being mindful of the commercial realities of publishing, it is my hope that a success here will lead to a more varied presentation of titles so that the full spectrum of contemporary filmmaking will be represented.

R.J.A.

I WOULD LIKE TO THANK THE FOLLOWING INDIVIDUALS
WHOSE COOPERATION HAS HELPED MAKE
THIS BOOK A REALITY.

Woody Allen	Peter Gardiner	Tony Hom	Tony Lover	Percy Schultz
Jack Artenstein	Bob Goodfried	Charles Joffe	Alyne Model	Grace Shaw
Madeline Borak	Josephine Graff	Ulla Käkönen	Anastasia Nicole	Alexander Soma
Nancy Carey	Regina Gruss	Diane Keaton	Carol Pokuta	Pamela Tarrabe
Harry Chester	Paul Haggar	Norma Lee	Susan Ann Protter	George Watters
Judith Crist	Nancy Hardin	Mario Leone	Jack Rollins	Nat Weiss
Bart Farber	Mark Henry	Howard Levine	Herbert Ross	Emmy Wexer
Al Fusco	Ryan Herz	Lois Lipfield	Irving Ross	

"It's still the
same old story,
a fight for
love and glory."*

Paramount Pictures presents

An Arthur P. Jacobs Production in association
with Rollins-Joffe Productions

"PLAY IT AGAIN, SAM"

A Herbert Ross Film

starring

WOODY ALLEN DIANE KEATON TONY ROBERTS
JERRY LACY and SUSAN ANSPACH JENNIFER SALT and VIVA as Jennifer

co-starring

Screenplay by **WOODY ALLEN** Produced by **ARTHUR P. JACOBS** Directed by **HERBERT ROSS** Executive Producer **CHARLES H. JOFFE**
Based on the play by **WOODY ALLEN** Produced on the New York stage by David Merrick Music Scored by Billy Goldenberg An APJAC Production Technicolor® A Paramount Picture

SOUNDTRACK ALBUM AVAILABLE ON PARAMOUNT RECORDS   *AS TIME GOES BY by Herman Hupfeld Copyright ©1931 by Harms, Inc. Copyright renewed. All rights reserved. Used by permission of Warner Brothers Music

PG PARENTAL GUIDANCE SUGGESTED
SOME MATERIAL MAY NOT BE
SUITABLE FOR PRE-TEENAGERS

Paramount
A Gulf + Western Company

Official: Allo, allo? Radio Tower? Lisbon plane taking off in ten minutes. East runway. Thank you.

Rick: Louis—have your man go with Mister Laszlo and take care of his luggage.

Renault: Certainly, Rick; anything you say.

Renault: Find Mr. Laszlo's luggage and put it on the plane.

Official: Yes, sir.

Official: This way, please, sir. **Rick:** If you don't mind, you fill in the names.

Rick: That'll make it even more official.
Renault: You think of everything, don't you?

Rick: And the names are Mr. and Mrs. Victor Laszlo.

Ilsa: But why my name, Richard?

Rick: 'Cause you're getting on that plane.
Ilsa: I don't understand; what about you?

Rick: I'm staying here with him till the plane gets safely away.

Ilsa: No, Richard, no! What has happened to you. Last night we said . . .
Rick: Last night we said a great many things.

Rick—You said I was to do the thinking for both of us. Well, I've done a lot of it since then and it all adds up to one thing. You're getting on that plane with Victor where you belong.

Ilsa: But, Richard, no, I . . .
Rick: Now you've got to listen to me.

Rick: Do you have any idea what you'd have to look forward to if you stayed here? Nine chances out of ten we'd both wind up in a concentration camp,—

Rick—isn't that true, Louis?

Renault: I'm afraid Major Strasser would insist.

Ilsa: You're saying this only to make me go.
Rick: I'm saying it because it's true.

Rick—Inside of us, we both know you belong with Victor.

Rick—You're part of his work, the thing that keeps him going. If that plane leaves the ground and you're not with him, you'll regret it.

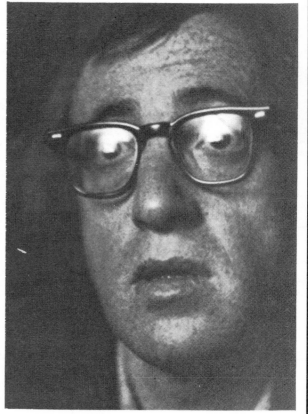

Ilsa: What about us?

Rick—Maybe not today, maybe not tomorrow, but soon, and for the rest of your life.

Rick: We'll always have Paris. If we didn't have, we'd—we'd lost it until you came to Casablanca. We got it back last night.

Ilsa: I said I would never leave you.
Rick: And you never will.

Rick: Look, I'm no good at being noble, but it doesn't take much to see that the problems of three little people don't amount to a hill of beans in this crazy world.

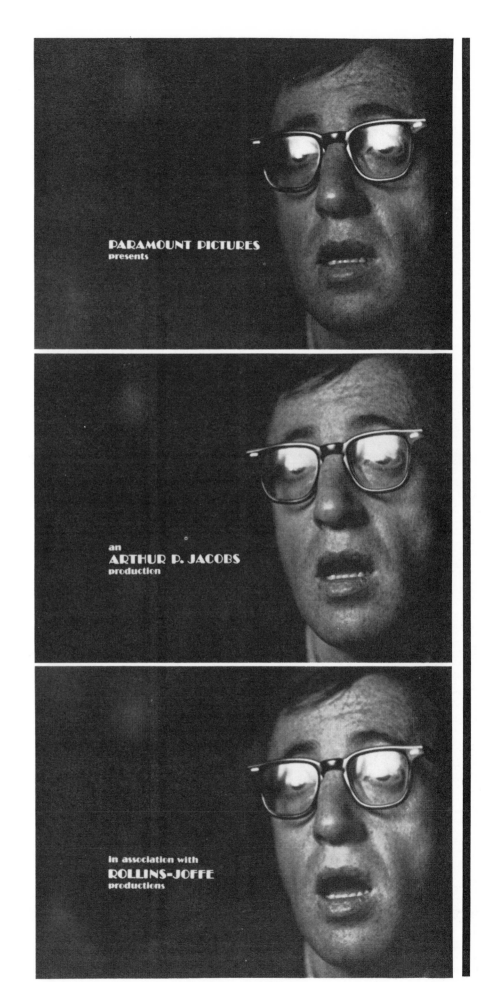

PARAMOUNT PICTURES
presents

an
ARTHUR P. JACOBS
production

in association with
ROLLINS-JOFFE
productions

Rick—Some day you'll understand that.

Rick: Now, now.

Rick: Here's looking at *you*, kid.

PLAY IT AGAIN, SAM

a
HERBERT ROSS
film

Rick: There's something you should know before you leave.

Laszlo: Mister Blane, I don't ask you to explain anything.

Rick: I'm going to anyway because it may make a difference to you later on.

Rick—You said you knew about Ilsa and me.
Laszlo: Yes.
Rick: But you didn't know she was at my place last night when you were.

Rick—She came there for the Letters of Transit. Isn't that true, Ilsa?
Ilsa: Yes.

Rick: She tried everything to get them and nothing worked. She did her best to convince me that she was still in love with me.

Rick—That was all over long ago.

Rick—For your sake she pretended it wasn't and—I let 'er pretend.
Laszlo: I understand.

Rick: Here it is.
Laszlo: Thanks.

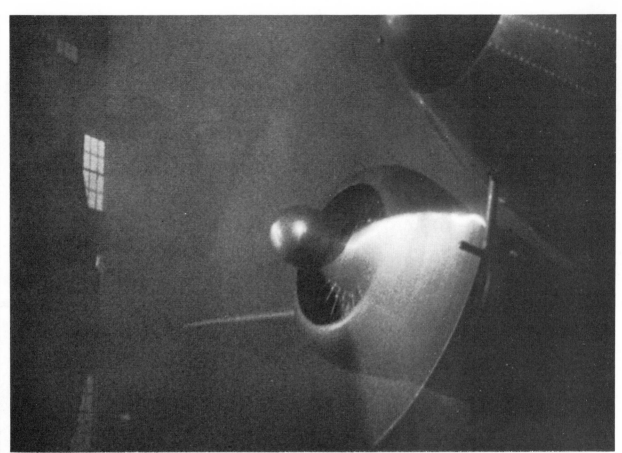

Laszlo: Are you ready, Ilsa?
Ilsa: Yes I'm ready.

co-starring
JENNIFER SALT
JOY BANG
and
VIVA as Jennifer

Ilsa: Goodbye, Rick. God bless you.

with
SUZANNE ZENOR
DIANA DAVILA
MARI FLETCHER

Rick: Better hurry or you'll miss that plane.

production supervisor
ROGER M. ROTHSTEIN

associate producer
FRANK CAPRA, JR.

Renault: It might be a good idea for you to disappear from Casablanca for a while.

based on the play by
WOODY ALLEN

Renault—There's a Free French garrison over at Brasaville. I could be of use to arrange a passage.
Rick: My Letter of Transit?

produced on the
New York stage by
DAVID MERRICK

Rick—I could use a trip. But it doesn't make any difference about our bet; you still owe me ten thousand francs.

executive producer
CHARLES JOFFE

Renault: And that ten thousand francs *should* pay our expenses.
Rick: *Our* expenses?
Renault: Mmmhmm.

screenplay by
WOODY ALLEN

Rick: Louis—I think this is the beginning of a beautiful friendship.

produced by
ARTHUR P. JACOBS

directed by
HERBERT ROSS

Allan:
Who'm I
kidding?
I'm not like
that. I never
was, I never
will be.

Allan—Strictly
the movies.

Allan: Ahhh I'm so depressed. Maybe if I took two more aspirin it would help.

Allan: 'Cept that would make—two—four—six—aspirin.

Allan—I'm turning into an aspirin junkie.

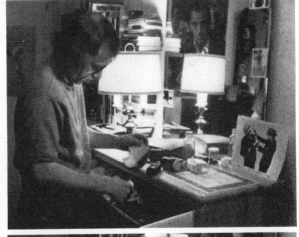

Allan—Next thing you know I'll be boiling the cotton at the top of the bottle to get the extra.

Nancy: I don't want any alimony. You can have everything; I just want out.

Allan: I never should've signed those papers.

Allan: Let 'er take me to court. Two years of marriage down the drain like that.

Allan—I couldn't believe what she said to me. She was like a stranger, not like my wife;— like a total stranger.

Allan: Well can't we discuss it?
Nancy: We discussed it fifty times; it's no use.

Allan: Why?

Nancy: I don't know. I can't stand the marriage. I don't find you any fun; I feel you suffocate me; I don't feel any rapport with you and I don't dig you physically.

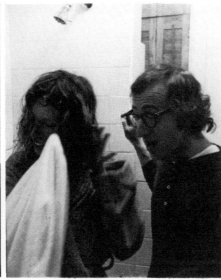

Nancy—Oh for God's sake, Allan, don't take it personal.

Allan: I won't take it personal.

Allan—I'll just kill myself that's all.

Allan: If only I knew where my damn analyst was vacationing. Where do they go every August? They leave the city. Every summer the city is full of people who are crazy till Labor Day.

Allan: So what if I reach 'im? What's he gonna tell me? No matter what I say he tells me it's a sexual problem.

Allan—Isn't that ridiculous. How can it be a sexual problem? We weren't even having relations.

Allan—Maybe once in a while.

Allan—She used to watch television during it. Change channels with the remote control switch.

Allan: Why should a divorce bother me so? What th' hell, maybe I'm better off without 'er.

Allan: Why not? I'm young, I'm healthy; I got a good job. This could be my chance to step out a little bit.

Allan—If she can swing so can I. I'll turn this place into a nightclub; I'll get broads up here like you wouldn't believe. Swingers, freaks, nymphomaniacs— dental hygienists.

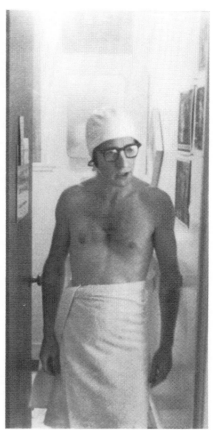

Allan—She don't want me, I'm not gonna push myself on 'er.

Allan—I couldn't believe what she said to me the day that she left.

33

Nancy: I want a new life. I wanta go skiing; I wanta go dancing; I wanta go to the beach.

Nancy—I wanta ride through Europe on a motorcycle. All we ever do is see movies.

Allan: You know I write for a film magazine; they *send* me. Besides I happen to like movies.

Nancy: You like movies because you're one of life's great watchers. I'm not like that, I'm a doer. I wanta live; I wanta participate. We never laugh together.

Allan: How can you say that? I don't know about you but I'm constantly laughing.
Nancy: Yeah.
Allan: I chuckle; I giggle; I guffaw occasionally.

Allan—Why didn't any of this come up when we were dating?
Nancy: Oh things were different then. You were more aggressive.

Allan: Everybody is during courtship. It's only natural. You try and impress the other person. You can't expect me to keep up that level of charm; I'd have a heart attack.

Nancy: Goodbye, Allan.

Nancy: My lawyer will call your lawyer!   **Allan:** I don't have a lawyer.   **Allan**—Have 'im call my doctor.

Allan: What's the matter with me? Why can't I be cool? What's the secret?

Bogart:
There's no secret, kid. Dames are simple. I never met one that didn't understand a slap in the mouth or a slug from a forty-five.

Allan:
Yeah 'cause you're Bogart. I could never hit Nancy; it's not that type of relationship.

Bogart:
Relationship? Now where'd ya learn that word? From one o' those Park Avenue headshrinkers?

Allan:
I'm not like you. At th' end o' *Casablanca* when you lost Ingrid Bergman weren't you crushed?

Bogart:
Nothin' a little bourbon and soda wouldn't fix.

Allan: Look I can't drink. My body will not tolerate alcohol.

Bogart: Take my advice, kid, and forget all this fancy relationship stuff. The world is full o' dames. All you gotta do is—whistle.

Allan: He's right. Ya give 'em an inch and they step all over ya.

Allan: Why can't I develop that attitude?

Allan— Nothin' a little—bourbon and soda couldn't fix.

Allan: She wants to laugh. She doesn't laugh enough. Insufficient laughter, that's grounds for divorce.

Dick: Allan, are you all right?

Linda: You poor thing.
Dick: Why didn't you call us as soon as she left?

Allan—And skiing, she wants to go skiing. She wants to ski down a mountain laughing like an idiot.

Allan: I didn't want to bother you.
Dick: Not bother us! For God's sakes, Allan, what are friends for?
Linda: What reason did she give for wanting a divorce?

Dick: Allan, lemme just call my office and tell 'em where I am. I ran out of a business meeting the minute you called; they musta thought I was crazy.

Linda: Have you heard from 'er?

Allan: I heard from the firm of Schulman and Weiss. They had me sign some papers and Nancy went to Mexico.

Allan: It's funny, we went to Mexico on our honeymoon. Spent the entire two weeks in bed.

Allan—I had dysentery.

Dick: Hello, George? Did they agree to the terms? Oh hell . . . Well if we blow it, we blow it.

Linda: My God, can't you cook anything but Teevee dinners?

Allan: Who bothers to cook 'em? I suck 'em frozen.

Dick: Lemme tell you where you can reach me, George; I'll be at uh— three six two, nine two nine six for a while. Then I'll be at six four eight, oh oh two four for about fifteen minutes, then I'll be at seven five two, oh four two oh and then I'll be home, at six two one, four five nine eight. Yeah. Right, George. Byebye.

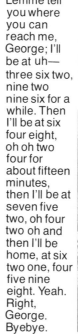

Linda: Uhh there's a phone booth on the corner; do you want me to run downstairs and get the number? You'll be passing it.

Allan—A dollar fifty on a thirty-five cent check.
Dick: All right, Allan, Nancy was impulsive. We all knew that about her.

Dick: I'm sorry, Allan.
Allan: She wants to be a swinger. All of a sudden married life is not good for her.

Allan: Yeah but she didn't leave impulsively. She talked about it for months. I just couldn't believe she'd go through with it.

Dick: Okay, don't get all worked up.
Allan: I gave her a home and affection and security. This is a little girl I found waiting on tables at The Hip Bagel.

Dick: Now look, it's good you found out now, Allan. I mean you're young; you can both make new lives.

Allan—I used to go in there every night and *over*tip 'er.

Allan: I'm now twenty-nine. The height of my sexual potency was ten years ago.

41

Dick: Oh, Allan, look at the bright side. You're free. You'll go out; there'll be girls.

Dick—You'll go to parties. You'll have affairs with married women—sexual relations with girls of every race, creed and color.

Allan: Oh, you get tired o' that. Besides, those kind of things never happen to me.

Allan—I managed to fool one girl into loving me and now she's gone.

Dick: You see how he downgrades himself? Don't you think there are plenty o' women in the world who would fine him attractive?

Linda: Hmm?

Linda—Oh well yes, yes, of course.

Dick: Allan, the world is full of eligible women.

Allan: Yeah but not like Nancy. She was a lovely thing.

Linda: Oh, he really loved 'er. I feel like crying.

Dick: Why do you feel like crying? A man makes an investment, it doesn't pay off.

Allan: I used to lay in bed at night and watch 'er sleep.
Once in a while she'd wake up and catch me.
She'd let out a scream.

Linda: Could I get an aspirin? I'm getting a little headache.
Dick: Well he's having a breakdown and you're getting sick.

Allan: You want an aspirin too?

Linda: All right, don't get upset!

Dick: No!

Dick: I'm not getting upset; I just had a very rough day today that's all.

Allan: I ate all the aspirin; what about Darvon?

Linda: Oh that's okay. My analyst once suggested Darvon when I had migraines.

Linda: With mine on vacation I feel paralyzed.

Allan: I used to get migraines but my analyst cured me; now I get tremendous cold sores.

Dick: The two of you should get married and move into a hospital.

Linda: I still do; big ugly ones from tension.
Allan: Yeah I don't think analysis can help me; I may need a lobotomy.

Allan: You want a Fresca with the Darvon?
Linda: Oh, unless you have apple juice.

Allan: Apple juice and Darvon, it's fantastic together!

Dick: Uh, could I get a Coke with nothing in it?

Linda: Have you ever had Librium and tomato juice?

Allan: I'll get the pills.

Allan: N-n-no I haven't personally, but another neurotic tells me they're unbelievable.

Dick: Poor guy.
Linda: Mmm.

Dick: Allan, if there's anything we can do . . .

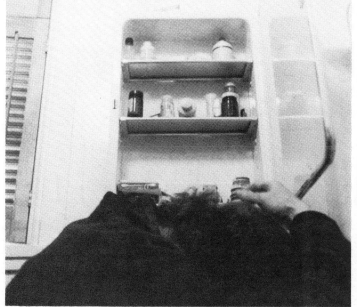

Linda: He never shoulda married Nancy.

Dick: He never mentioned anything; I thought they were getting along.

Linda: Oh it's because you're so busy all the time you never see what's going on around you.

Linda: See, these things upset me. I'm experiencing a wave of insecurity.

Dick: *You*'re experiencing a wave of insecurity? May I tell you what happened to me today?

Linda—Didn't you think it was a little strange that he was married and yet he still couldn't get a date on New Year's Eve?

Dick: Okay, darling, don't get overwrought.

Dick—I bought a hundred acres of land in Florida this morning; it turns out ninety-eight of them have quicksand. My syndicate wanted to build a golf course. Now what?

Dick—Hello, this is Mister Christie, I'm no longer at seven five two, oh four two oh, I'm gonna be home, that's six two one, four five nine eight. What? Yes, I'll hold on.

Dick—The only thing we can do is to build a three-hole golf course with the biggest sand trap in the world.

Dick: What're you taking a pill for?
Linda: It's a Milltown; I'm tense.

Dick: Why?
Linda: You know, honey, the whole subject of divorce is traumatic for me.

Dick: You're so insecure. I wish I could te . . .

Dick: Yeah but *he*'s getting divorced, not us.
Linda: It's the idea of it. I guess I've never gotten over my parents' divorce.

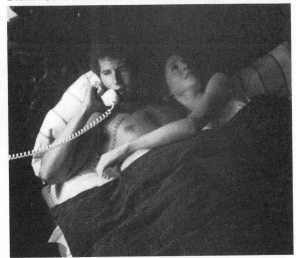

Dick—Hello, Milt? Dick. Listen—that deal is unacceptable; the figures are lousy.

Dick: It's about time. Come 'ere.
Linda: Ohhh.

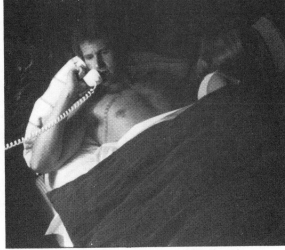

Dick—No I can't take it in that form, Milt; there's . . .

Man: All right, come out there now. Uh, Betty, you go back in.

Dick: Marjorie, did Mister Hardy call?

Dick: Ah ha. Well I'm at nine two two, three two nine nine. Yeah well I'll be here . . . I'm picking my wife up. What? Who? Oh, Allan Felix. Yeah all right, I'll call 'im later. Right. Byebye.

Dick—Allan's calling again.
Linda: Mmhmm.
Dick: We gotta find 'im a girl. Somebody he can *be* with and get excited about.
Linda: Well we oughta find a nice girl for 'im.

Dick: There must be somebody amongst all these women.
Linda: No, not that many single ones.
Dick: What about Carol?
Linda: Engaged.

Dick: What about *her*?
Linda: Doreen?
Dick: Yeah.
Linda: She's living with a priest.

Dick: How about the tall one with the blonde hair?
Linda: Coreda for Allan?
Dick: Mmmm.

Linda: My God, she'd eat 'im alive; there'd be nothing left but his glasses. No, uh-uh, I think this is going to be a little bit of a problem.

Secretary: Mister Christie—
Dick: Yeah?
Secretary: There's a call for you.

Allan: No; I haven't looked at another woman in two years; I'm outa practice. When I was *in* practice I was outa practice.
Dick: Yes?

Dick: Look, I got a great idea. Linda and I are going out for dinner tonight. Uh we'll invite some nice girl and the four of us'll go together.
Allan: No . . .
Dick: Aw come on, Allan; you gotta get out and start meeting girls.

Dick: Allan, you've invested your emotions in a losing stock. It was wiped out. It dropped off the board. Now what do you do, Allan? You re-invest. Maybe in a more stable stock. Something with long-term growth possibilities.

Allan: Who are you gonna fix me up with, General Motors?
Dick: Aw come on, Allan, shape up. What kind of a girl do you like?

Allan: A pretty girl, because she'd have to be damn good to do anything for my morale at all.

Dick: Come on, darling, who can we get for 'im?
Allan: You mean you don't even have anybody in mind?
Dick: Yes, we have several people in mind.
Linda: What kind do you like, Allan?

Dick: He likes neurotics.

Allan: No. I like blondes. Little blondes with long hair and short skirts and boots —

Allan—and big chests and bright and witty and perceptive.

Dick: Well don't set yourself ridiculous standards, Allan.
Linda: She must be beautiful with long hair and a big bust?

Allan: Yes, and a good behind. Something I can sink my teeth into.

Dick: He was always very fussy.

Allan: Right! But look at the result.

52

Dick: Right! You never went out.
Linda: Sally Keller has long hair and a good-sized chest.

Allan: Yeah, what's good-sized?

Linda: I dunno—like this, I guess.

Dick: She's not the brightest girl in the world, Allan.
Allan: What does she do?
Linda: She works for an astrologer.

Allan: Forget it.
Dick: Aw come on, Allan, you might even get *her* into bed.
Allan: In bed. With my luck I won't be able to get her into a *chair*.

Linda: Well the girls with the looks that you want usually don't have great minds.

Dick: I don't know why we're making such a fuss over a little pleasant dinner companionship.
Allan: Hey look, I don't even want *that*; I can't go out. I'm still attached to Nancy.
Dick: Allan, will you forget about Nancy?

Dick: She's gone.
Allan: That's true.

Allan—She wanted to be free so she could swing.
Dick: Come on, darling, think of somebody.
Linda: Mmm . . .
Allan: I can just picture what *she*'s up to.

Nancy: Oh ho, baby, this is wonderful! My ex-husband would never take me on a motorcycle. He fell off a scooter once. And broke his collar bone.

Nancy—I don't mean a motor scooter either, I mean the kind you push with your foot. Movies, that's his whole life. He's a watcher.
Man: I'm a doer.

Nancy: Oh, it's been so long since I've been made love to by a tall, strong, handsome, blue-eyed, blond man.

Allan: We're divorced two weeks; she's dating a Nazi.

Linda: Sharon Lake, she works for Jack Edelman the photographer; she's his assistant.
Dick: She's a bright girl and very cute.

Allan: Let's go!

Linda: Hey, what about Sharon?
Dick: Yeah, yeah, what about Sharon?
Allan: I like the name.

Dick: Call 'er.
Linda: Perfect.

Allan: Wait a minute; what're you gonna tell 'er?
Linda: I'm just going to see if she's free for dinner.

Allan: Well don't say anything about the divorce. 'er my wife's dead.

Dick: Leave it us us, huh?
Allan: Wait a minute. I don't know if we should go through with this now; the old tension's beginning to set in. My stomach is jumping.
Linda: Ahh Sharon Lake please. Yeah, Linda Christie.

Allan: I don't wanta hear this. Oooo—Eeee—Oooo!
Linda: Sharon? Linda. How are ya? Uh—fine.
Allan: Oooo—Eeee—Oooo!

Allan: Oooo—Eeee—Oooo!
Linda— Listen. Dick and I are going to dinner tonight with an old friend and we thought you might want to join us.
Allan: Oooo—Eeee—Oooo!

Dick: Shut up, shut up!
Linda: No, no no, that's nothing; we just have the radio on.
Dick: Shhhh!

Linda:
Al-Allan
Felix. No,
you don't
know him,
he's . . .

Allan—
I don't
need this
aggravation.

Allan:
A writer.
A widower,
a widower;
tell 'er my
wife died in
a mine shaft
explosion.
Linda: Oh
he is, he's
lots of fun. I
think you'll
like him.

Linda: Oh,
oh okay.
We'll pick
you up with
the car, eight
o'clock. Oh,
a simple
dress. Sure—
flats are okay.

Allan: Look
if she doesn't
wanta do it,
forget it.

Allan: Let 'er
wear heels.
What am I,
Toulouse-
Lautrec?
Linda: Okay.
Byebye.

Linda: You're set.

Allan: Ohhh, I really have mixed feelings about this! What if I have this chick in bed and Nancy comes walking back?

Dick: Let's not hope for too much this first night, Allan.

Allan: Did she say anything about me?
Linda: What could she say? She doesn't even know you.

Allan: Well you never said that I was a widower.
Linda: Now look—I got you the date, you tell her the part about your wife's death.

Allan: I'm excited about this!

Dick: Now look, we'll pick Sharon up first 'cause she lives near us and we'll get you at about ten after eight. I can't stay out late though, darling; I gotta get up early for a business meeting.

Allan: You know we can eat out at the Pier in Sausalito. It's a perfect night to dine out.
Linda: Oh, wonderful—it's so romantic.

Dick: Oh, the food is terrible there; besides I think it's gonna rain. You gonna be all right?

Allan: I'm gonna be fine. I'm gonna shower and douse my body with Canoe.

Allan—I'm goin' home. I think today I'm gonna brush *all* my teeth.

Linda: Oohh.
Dick: I think he and Sharon oughta hit it off, don't you?
Linda: Yeah?
Dick: Oh you don't think so?
Linda: Uh—well he'll probably calm down later tonight.

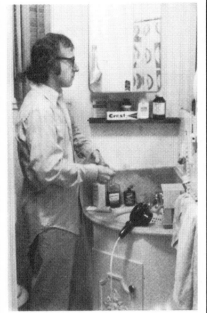

Allan: I wish she'd seen me before. I hate to be there on a blind date with a girl who first sets eyes on me.

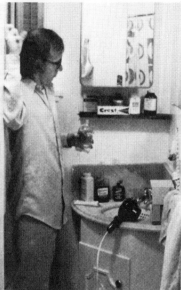

Allan: If she's disappointed and she—laughs or—screams.

Allan: Ridiculous. Has a girl ever once reacted by laughing or screaming?

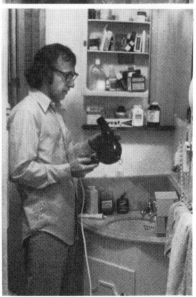

Allan: Once. A little coed from Brooklyn College—came to the door, saw me and passed out. She was weak from dieting though.

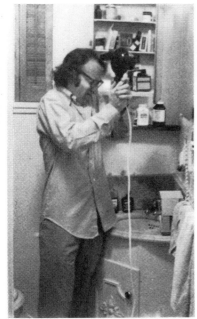

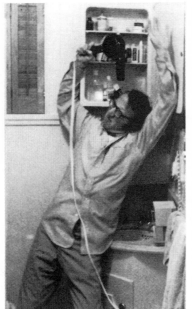

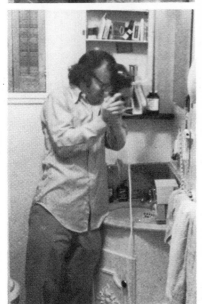

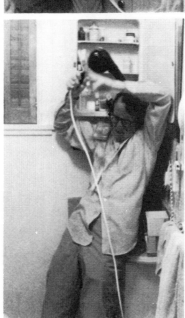

Allan: Oh. What th' hell.

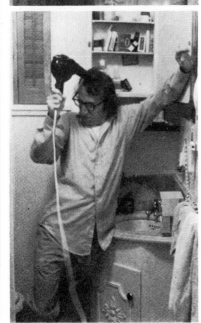

Allan: Bogart was short. That never seemed to bother anybody.
Bogart: You're startin' off on the wrong foot, kid.

Bogart: Sure. You're lettin' her get the best of ya before the game even starts.

Allan: Yeah, negative y'mean.

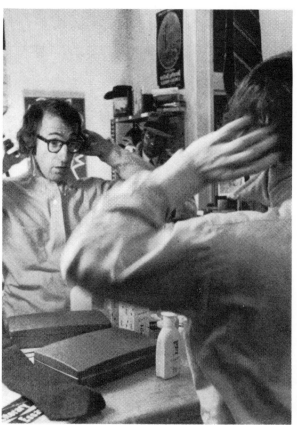

Bogart—Say what's that stuff you was puttin' on your face?
Allan: That's Canoe; it's an after-shave lotion.
Bogart: Yeah? What about all that other stuff?

Allan: Uhh that's Lavoris, Mennen's Spray Deodorant and Johnson and Johnson baby powder.

Bogart: For Chrissake, kid; you're gonna smell like a French cat house.

Allan: I need them.

Bogart: Why? You ashamed to sweat?

Allan: I want to make an impression.

Bogart: You know, kid—somewheres in life you got turned around. It's *her* job to smell nice for *you*. And whatever you do don't tell her you don't drink. She'll think you're a Boy Scout. And don't get nervous. The only bad break you could get is if she turns out to be a virgin. Or a cop.

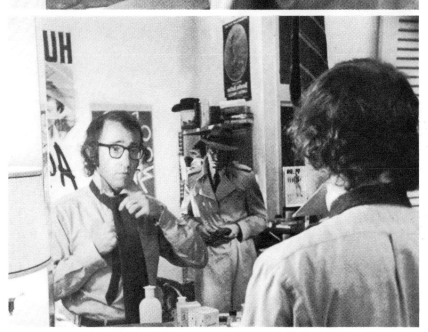

Allan: With my luck she'll turn out to be both. I know he's right. A lotta women are—turned on by a masculine, earthy quality. I shouldn't'a put so much Binaca under my arms. Wouldn't it be great if Sharon and I hit it off at first sight.

63

Allan—
Why not?
They—they say
that dames
are simple.

Allan—
I never met one
who didn't
understand a
slap in the mouth
or a slug from
a forty-five.

Allan:
Come 'ere,
Sharon.

Sharon:
Oh, Allan . . .
you are fantastic!
Up until tonight,
the doctors had
told me that I was
frigid.

Sharon—
Oh, I want to
thank you for
proving them
wrong.

Allan:
If you got any girl
friends with the
same problem
bring 'em over.

Sharon:
When Dick
and Linda spoke
of you, they used
terms like—
brilliant and—

Sharon—
But they
didn't say that
you were
also an animal.

Allan:
Sorry I had to
slap ya around,
sweetheart.
But you got
hysterical
when I said,
'no more'.

Sharon:
Oh, Allan . . .
oh, Allan . . .

Allan: Yes?
Linda: It's Linda.
Allan: Linda?

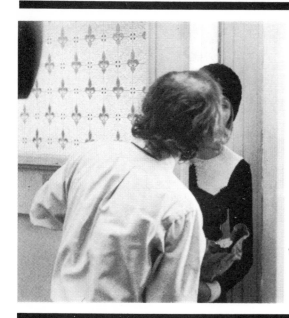

Linda:
Yes. I'm alone. Sharon's with Dick; they're out parking; they sent me ahead just to make sure everything's okay.

Allan:
Everything's fine; I didn't realize it was so late.

Linda:
Hey, what'd you do? break a bottle of shaving lotion?

Allan:
You're kidding. I'm wearing too much?

Linda:
Well it's a touch strong, not terrible though.

Linda—Once we get out into the air you won't even notice it.

Allan:
I—better set this place up quickly.

Linda: The place is fine. We're just going to have a quick drink and go.

Allan: A few carefully placed objects will create the proper impression.

Linda: You're not going to leave those half-open books lying around like you're reading them?

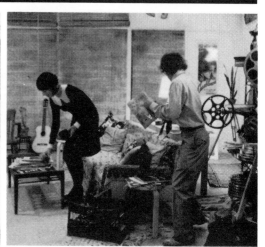

Allan: Why not? It creates an image.

Linda:
Allan, you don't
need an image.
Allan: See?
Linda: Uh huh.

Allan:
Got just the
thing, my
hundred yard
dash medal.

Linda: Oh you're joking; you're not going to leave out a track medal.

Allan: Why not? I paid twenty dollars for it.

Allan:
I got a big
decision to
make here.

Linda: Yeah.

Allan:
Do I go with
Oscar Peterson
or Bartok's String
Quartet Number
Five?

Linda: Why
don't you play
your Oscar
Peterson and
leave Bartok
out so that
everybody
can see it?

Allan: That's a good idea.

Linda: You know I have never seen anybody go to so much trouble to impress a date. Particularly such a casual date.

Linda—I mean if you devoted this much time and interest with Nancy I don't see why she left you.

Allan: I did. I used to write 'er poems and, take her to candle-light restaurants and order in French. And the waiter would bring all the wrong things.

Linda: Maybe if you just leaned across the candlelight and kissed 'er . . .

Allan: I tried. She used to say 'Christ, not here; everybody's staring.' And once at a little bistro in Union Street my sleeve caught fire.

You laugh; it's funny, right? She took it as a symbol of my clumsiness which I guess it was.

Linda: Oh!

Allan: Tremendous poise.

Allan: I'm an absolute master.

Linda: Hi, come on in. Come on in.

Dick: Allan—this is Sharon.
Sharon: Hello.

Sharon: I was just telling Dick I've got friends on this block; in the house right across the street; d'you know the Gibsons?
Allan: Gibsons? No.
Sharon: Hal and Eleanor Gibson. They're a fantastic couple; he's an interior decorator.

Allan: Oh really? That's—sort of a hobby of mine.

Sharon: Oh. Uh huh.

Allan: The—key to interior decorating is to avoid looking like you used a decorator.

Dick: Gotta make one quick call.

Sharon: Linda—are you wearing jasmine?

Linda: Me? No.

Linda—Well let's see now, what're we drinking?

Dick: I'll have a J and B on the rocks.
Sharon: I'll have a little Harvey's Bristol Cream, please.
Allan: I'll have the usual.

Allan—Bourbon and water.

Sharon: Oh, a bourbon man.

Allan: I gotta cut down on my drinkin'; I'm—I'm beginnin' to put away a quart a day.

CRAAASH!!

Dick: This is Mister Christie, uh—I'm no longer at four three one, five nine nine seven; I'm gonna be at Mister Fe . . . What time did that come in?

Linda: Sharon did a movie.
Allan: Oh?
Sharon: Underground.

Allan: Stag film?
Sharon: Underground. You know very arty, sixteen millimeter.
Linda: Yes well Allan's interested in cinema.
Sharon: Oh really? Whadda ya do?
Allan: A writer. Nothing much but—'Film Weekly' uh—articles, essays, criticisms—

Sharon: Oh, this film I did got very good reviews. As a matter of fact I got singled out. Of course I *was* the only girl in it with nine men.

Allan: Really? What was it called? Maybe I saw it.

Sharon: *Gang Bang*.

Sharon—You know these films have the raunchiest titles. Really it wasn't a bit sexy.

Linda: You were all out of bourbon so I made it straight water.

Linda—Well, it's so humid out, I think it's going to rain.
Sharon: Maybe that's why I've got this headache. I get terrible sinus attacks.
Allan: You should have 'em drained.

Dick: That's why it's silly to go to the Pier.
Sharon: Do you think you could turn the music down a little bit?
Allan: Of course.

Dick: What's the point of goin' to an outdoor restaurant if it's gonna rain?
Linda: You used to like to take me walking in the rain.

Allan: I love the rain. It washes memories off the sidewalk of life.

SCRAAATCH!!

Linda: Oh!

Linda: Gee, Allan, you really have a delicate touch.

Dick: Allan is a trifle tense. He had a little misfortune with his wife.
Linda: Dick!
Sharon: His *wife*?

Dick: Well his ex-wife. She's gone.
Allan: She's dead!
Sharon: How awful.
Linda: Well no, she's not really dead.

Allan: No no—technically not dead; we're not dating.

Dick: She left him.
Sharon: I'm sorry.

Allan: Oh that's all. . . .

Sharon: Is he *on* anything?

Linda: Well he's been under some strain lately.

Dick: Hi, this is Mister Christie, I'm at the Hong Fat Noodle Company uh uh that's uh—eight two four, seven nine nine six. Yeah, right. Byebye.

Allan: Lemme tell ya what's really interesting. Is when they eat—when they eat uh—rice with chopsticks authentically,—

Allan—they kinda bring it up to their mouth like this and they—it's kind of a shoveling move that you get with your arm, y'know, just sort of . . .

Allan: What's the matter?
Sharon: Would you excuse me a second? I'll be right back.

Allan: She likes me.
Linda: What?

Allan: I can read women. She wants me to come on with her. She digs me. She's playing it very cool. I'm gonna come on with her later.

Sharon: Well, good night and thanks for dinner.
Allan: It's only ten o'clock.
Sharon: Well I've got this headache and I've really gotta get up early tomorrow.
Allan: Oh, I'll walk you upstairs; come on.
Sharon: That's okay.
Allan: No no no, honey; this city's a jungle. I better go.

Sharon: Well—good night.

Allan—If I'm not down in an hour, sublet my apartment.

Allan: You know, Sharon—a dame like you—

Dick: You know any other girls?
Linda: I don't know if any of my friends are his type. Most of the girls I know are fairly normal.
Dick: He's just over-anxious, that's all.
Linda: As soon as she came over he went into his act.

Allan—and a guy like. . . .

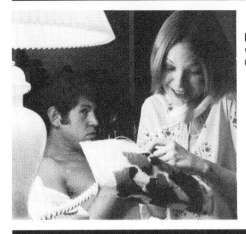

Linda: How'd it go with Sharon? Oh—oh really? Oh . . .

Allan: I keep striking out with women and you keep laughing.

Linda: No but everybody's insecure, Allan, not just you. No no, you're wrong; Dick *is*. Oh come on, me? are you kidding? Ask my analyst.

Allan: How many times a week do you go?
Linda: Three. But the one of them is Group.
Allan: Is there anyone in your group that would be good for me, you know? Like emotionally disturbed women are sort of interesting usually. Maybe a nice pervert or something?

Allan: Jennifer? What do you mean crazy?
Linda: Well it-it'll strictly be sex. You know she's too weird to have a relationship with.

Allan: Yeah well I don't mind just sex. That'd be great. You know I-I think I'd prefer a girl that didn't get hung up on me.

Allan: Yes, I definitely think we should try it, you know? And I really appreciate this, I-I know it must be a drag for you. You know who's not insecure, Bogart.
Linda: But, Allan, that's not real life. I mean you set too high a standard.

Allan: Lookit, if you're gonna identify who'm I gonna pick? my rabbi? I think Bogart's a perfect image.
Linda: You don't have to pick anybody; you're you. I know that you can't believe that. Anyway—onward to Jennifer.

Allen: Phew!

Jennifer: Allan, I won't deny it.

Jennifer: I'm a nymphomaniac.

Jennifer—I discovered sex very early. I slept with everybody. My school teacher—my sister's husband—the String Section of the New York Philharmonic.

Jennifer—I wanted to have sex all the time. *Play* all the time. Otherwise you're just down. And well why be down? The best way to get *up* is sex.

Jennifer—I'm not like my sisters. They're so inhibited, they never want to do anything. I believe in having sex as often, as freely, and as intensely as possible.

Jennifer:
What do you
take me for?

Allan:
How did I
misread
those signs?

Linda: This stuff just knocks me out. Do you realize we're in a room that holds some of the highest achievements of Western civilization?
Allan: Yeah but there's no girls.
Linda: Yeah. Oh, look at that wall, look; oh!
Allan: That's pretty.
Linda: Yeah. If you could have any painting, what would you pick?
Allan: Uh—a Van Gogh, any Van Gogh.

Linda: Yeah. Me too. I feel some sort of mystical attraction for Van Gogh. Why is that?
Allan: I dunno. I just know he was a great painter and he cut off his ear for a girl that he loved.
Linda: That's the kind of thing *you*'d do for a girl.
Allan: I'd really have to like 'er a lot.
Linda: I wonder if Dick would cut his ear off for me.
Allan: I don't think you oughta ask him; he's been very busy lately.

Linda: Must be fantastic to be loved so intensely. Ahhh.
Allan: Why don't we split and see if there's any action up at the Berkeley Museum?
Linda: Okay.
Allan: This is ridiculous.

Linda: Hey, hey, Allan, there's one.

Allan: Oh, she's great!
Linda: Go ahead, Allan; speak to her.
Allan: Nooo, are you kidding?

Linda: No no no, go on before the room gets . . .
Allan: . . . public museum?
Linda: Come on, go on, give it a try.
Allan: What'm I gonna say?
Linda: That's what we're here for, Allan. Go on, go on.
Allan: Casual, casual.
Linda: Okay.

Allan: That's quite a lovely Jackson Pollack, isn't it?

Woman: Yes it is.

Allan: What does it say to *you*?

Woman: It re-states the negativeness of the universe. The hideous lonely emptiness of existence. Nothingness. The predicament of Man forced to live in a barren, Godless eternity like a tiny flame flickering in an immense void with nothing but waste, horror and degradation, forming a useless bleak straitjacket in a black absurd cosmos.

Allan: What're you doing Saturday night?

Allan: What about Friday night?

Woman: Committing suicide.

Allan: If they're beautiful they're crazy, y'know? Great beauty drives a woman crazy.

Linda: What's he ranting about?

Allan: What am I going to the beach for anyhow? I hate the beach. I don't like swimming, I don't like the sun. I'm red-headed, I'm fair-skinned; I don't tan, I stroke.

Dick: A lotta good women go to the beach weekends, you know that.

Allan: Secretaries, receptionists.

Linda: Ahhh.

Allan: I want a really, really great woman.

Linda: Yeah, well look Madame Curie's dead; who else is there?

Allan: I thought you were too busy to go away on the weekend.

Dick: Ah a couple of guys from the office are gonna be there; I got a few meetings lined up.

Linda: Oh, well do you think there'll be a chance to see you while you're up there?

Dick: I got you pencilled in for dinner.

Linda: Ah hah, very funny. Very funny.

Allan: Are there spiders at the beach?

Dick & Linda: Aw come on, Allan . . .

Allan: I mean it. Anything with more than two legs and it walks across my chest, kills me.

Linda: Honey, we gotta find 'im a broad.

Dick: That's for sure.

Linda: We gotta find 'im some broad anyway.

Allan: I'm carsick.

Linda & Dick: Ohhh, come on, Allan!

Dick: We're gonna drop ya in the Bay.

Dick: Hello, this is Mister Christie. I'm no longer at seven three one, oh seven one one—I'll be at eight eight five, oh seven one four. That's good for the whole weekend.

Allan: This is terrific. This's a terrific beach house.
Linda: Oh I'm glad you like it.
Allan: Yeah, let's burn it down for the insurance.

Dick: Byebye.
Allan: Hey, there's a single bed in here! What happens if I get lucky?
Linda: Oh, you make love on the beach.

Allan: On the beach?
Linda: Yeah.
Allan: I'll be making love in the sand and the tide'll come in and carry me off, and I'll score and drown at the same time.

Allan: Oh, look at *that*. That is pretty. Look out there.
Linda: Ohh yeah.

Allan: Ohh it's really beautiful. The fog's gonna creep in. Look—you can see the seagulls flying over the cesspool.

Linda: Hey, this is fun. We haven't been to a place like this in such a long time.

Allan: I'm getting a heart attack; I can't believe that girl.

Dick: I'm at three nine two, eight oh nine eight.

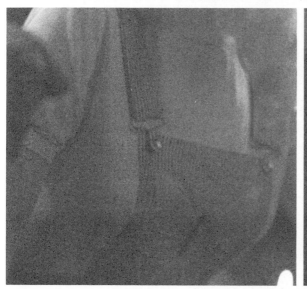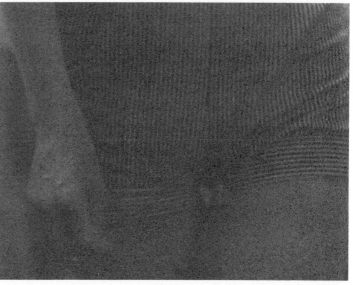

Allan: She's a doll. I would sell my mother to the Arabs for her.
Linda: Whyn't you ask her to dance? You've been staring at her for an hour.
Allan: I can't; I don't know 'er.

Dick: Darling, I can't stay here too much longer. I have to get up early tomorrow and play tennis with some of the guys from the office.
Linda: You wanta dance one dance, honey?
Dick: We can't do those dances, darling. You have to be under sixteen to look good.

Allan: I love you, Miss, whoever you are. I want to have your child.

Linda: All right, Allan; get up and do it.

Allan: No, I can't dance.
Linda: Come on.

Allan: I'm scared. I had. measles as a child; my body won't function.
Dick: Come on, Allan; go.

Linda: Now start dancing. Ya ready? Now keep time; it's one— two.
Allan: One, two.

Linda: Right. Now okay, now go ahead and say something to 'er.

Allan: . . . One, two. One, two. One, two. . . .

Linda: Allan, try something more meaningful.

Allan: Three, four. Three, four.

Linda: Speak to 'er, Allan.

Allan: You interested in dancing at all?

Girl: Get lost, creep.

Linda: What'd she say?
Allan: She'd rather not.
Linda: Ahhh.

Dick: Even if we buy two more lots we're still gonna have to wait to build.

1st Man: Well it's still cheaper to hold onto them.

2nd Man: It's not gonna stay at these prices indefinitely.

Dick: Well it'll require a loan and it'll require using our current holdings as collateral.

Linda: Don't you understand, Allan? You've got a lot going for you. You're bright—and you're funny and I think you're even romantic if you'd only believe it. I don't see why you put on a false mask every time you meet a girl.

2nd Man: Will we be able to build? Even in the new tax year?

Dick: Yeah but what's the point of doing it if the interest rate might go down in six months?

Linda: But, Allan, I keep telling you, whyn't you just be yourself; the girl will fall in love with you.

Allan: Y'know you've been great these past weeks spending your time with me, really.

Linda: Ahhh. Well I'll tell you the truth. I'm having a ball.

Allan: Are ya?

Linda: Yeah.

Dick: Oh, it'll make a big difference, Tom; if-if ya gonna pay if ya gonna pay six hundred dollars a lot . . .

2nd Man: . . . great opportunity . . .

1st Man: . . . new tax year you may have a half a per cent more interest rate.

Allan: Listen I—I got you a present 'cause I know it's your birthday.

Linda: But how'd you know?

Allan: You mentioned the date and I remembered it 'cause it's the—same date my mother had her hysterectomy.

Linda: Oh, Allan . . . Oh, it's lovely—beautiful. A plastic skunk.

Allan: Yeah it looked so cute in F.A.O. Schwartz' and I heard you say that skunks are your favorite animal.

Linda: I'm so touched I don't know what to say.

Allan: You really like it?

Linda: I love it.

Allan: Yeah I'm glad, 'cause it doesn't do anything; it's just a skunk, you know.

Dick: I think she liked your present better than mine.

Allan: Aw I don't think so.

Dick: I'm serious. She usually gets so excited whenever I get her anything. This time all she could talk about was her skunk.

Allan: It's your imagination.

Dick: I dunno. She's moody lately.

Allan: 'Cause you neglect 'er.

Dick: I know I neglect 'er. Why, did she say something?

Allan: She doesn't have to. I see the two of you together.

Dick: Yeah?

Allan: Yeah. Plus she said something.

Dick: It's probably nothing we haven't been through.

Allan: Well, she's really an insecure girl, you know? She needs attention . . .

Dick: What has she got to be insecure about? I'm crazy about her; she *knows* that. Why? Because I'm too busy at this particular time to always dote on her? You have to understand Linda, Allan. Because she's used to being fussed over. She's always very pretty, high marks in college.

I sometimes think the reason she married me was because I was one of the few guys who didn't fawn over her. Not that I don't want to.

Allan: Yeah but you must admit you're driven.

Dick: Hey, do you know what's happening with the stock market? Read the papers, Allan.

Allan: Where're we going?

Dick: All right, all right, all right. There she is. There she is.

Dick: She works in my office; I met 'er up here yesterday. Now uh she just broke off with her boyfriend.
Allan: Nooo—there's too many people at the table.

Dick: Aw come on, Allan; doesn't make any difference.
Allan: I don't think I wanta . . . No, we'll do it later.
Dick: Awhhh!
Allan: What do you want me to say?
Dick: Ask her to dinner.
Allan: No, I can't ask her to dinner now—why can't you and Linda come along?
Dick: Because I have to work tonight, that's why.

Dick: Julie—this is Allan Felix.

Allan: Would you like to go to dinner this evening?

Julie: . . . is he fast.

Dick: That's right to the point.

Allan: Look, I . . . forgive me—I'm—so . . . It needed tossing anyhow.

Julie:
Hey! Let's
go in there and
get stoned and
watch the freaks?

Allan:
Yeah? You sure
you don't want to go to
the movies 'cause
there's an Eric von
Stroheim festival . . .

Julie:
Come onnn!
Come on.

1st Rider: Wanna dance?
Allan: No, no thanks.

1st Rider: I didn't ask you; I asked her.
Allan: I-I-I don't wanta dance either.

1st Rider: What the hell is this?

Allan: Seven Up. I'm on the wagon now, doctor's orders—my hand shakes, I . . . battle fatigue,—

Allan—I . . . That kills me. Just . . .

1st Rider: What's your name, honey?
Julie: Julie.
1st Rider: Julie! It's a nice name, Julie.

Allan: Gotta get the kid back to the orphanage, y'know. I take 'er out once a year to the zoo and circus; we . . . Excuse me.

1st Rider: Sit down.

Allan: I'd love to stay but I gotta be up early tomorrow; go to temple. It's my people's sabbath.

1st Rider: Chris!
Allan: Uh—uh—Chris is coming over, isn't he?
1st Rider: Want ya to meet this good-lookin' broad.

2nd Rider: Hi.
Allan: Hi.
2nd Rider: Great to invite us over, uh?
Allan: Oh, just get right in here.
2nd Rider: I love . . . .

Allan: Yeah, guys.
1st Rider: You'd look real good on the back of my chopper.
2nd Rider: Ahh mmhmm.
Allan: You fellows seen the—the new production of *The Trojan Women* ? You're— uh—you're perfect.

Linda: What're you doing?

Dick: Financial reports. Which are not fun.

Linda: Have you seen Allan around lately?

Dick: No. Oh, he was here before. He's out tonight.

Linda: On a date?

Dick: Yes. I fixed 'im up.

Linda: You did?

Dick: Mmhmm.

Linda: Who with?

Dick: One of the girls in the office.

Linda: Ohhh. Which one?

Dick: Julie.

Linda: Julie? Which one is Julie? Do I know her?

Dick: Very sexy. And bright too. They're gonna like each other, that's my guess.

Linda: Is Julie uh the blonde one with big eyes?

Dick: Blonde, big eyes, very earthy, always wears those tight clothes with the see-through blouses. Every guy in the office has a thing for her.

Linda: Oh. Do you think she's right for Allan?

Dick: Mmhmm.

Linda: Yeah? 'Cause 'cause to me she doesn't seem like the type because . . .

Dick: No, he liked 'er.

Linda: Really?

Dick: Yeah.

Linda: How do *you* know?

Dick: I could feel it.

Linda: Did he say anything?

Dick: Hey. I'm tryin' to work.

Linda: Okay, I'm sorry.

Julie: Those guys are following us.
Allan: Don't worry about a thing; I'm a very fast runner.
2nd Rider: Hey, Ace, where you goin' with that chick?

1st Rider: Yeah.
Allan: Don't look back; I don't have my Bible.
Julie: I'm scared.
Allan: I better go into my fake limp.

1st Rider: Hey, let's all go on a little party, huh?
Allan: Fellas—fellas—I'm a veteran, I . . .

1st Rider: Why don't you get rid of this creep; come on, I'll take ya for a ride on my chopper.
2nd Rider: Yeah.

Allan: Hey, take your hands off her!

Allan: Ohh did somebody say that?
2nd Rider: All right, Shorty.

Allan: Here . . . your tattoo's coming off on my neck.

Julie: I'm gonna start screaming.
Allan: Don't worry, sweetheart; I can handle this.

Allan: All right, start screaming.

Linda: Allan, is that you?
Allan: Yes.

Dick: How'd it go, fella?
Allan: I got into a fight.

Dick: What? You got into a fight?
Allan: Yep.
Dick: With who?

Allan: Some guys were gettin' tough with Julie, I—had to teach 'em a lesson.
Dick: Are you all right?

Allan: Yeah, I'm fine, I—I snapped my chin down onto some guy's fist and hit another one in the knee with my nose.
Dick: Where's Julie?

Allan: Mmm—she ran off with the leader, I think they're gettin' married. They're headin' for Mexico now,—

Allan: I — It never woulda worked between Julie and me 'cause she's—Protestant and I'm Catholic and—there's a—great religious abyss between my . . .

Dick: Listen, who were these guys?

Allan: Oh . . . they said they were uh hairdressers. I . . . Hard to believe though, you know?

Dick: You want us to call a doctor?

Allan: No no, I'm fine. I-I could use a-a three-foot Band Aid on my body. . . . pain subsides . . .

Allan—Do you know what my sex life is turning into? The Petrified Forest. Hmm.

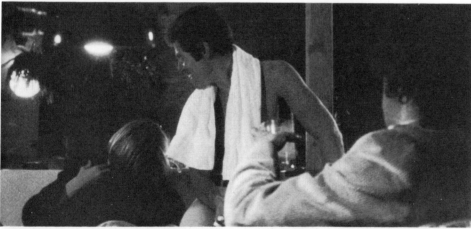

Allan: Very funny.

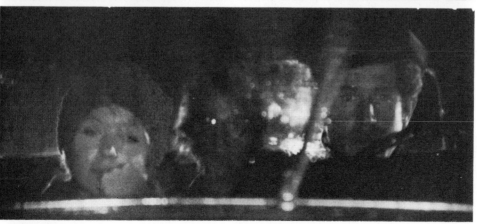

Allan: Ten million women in the country and I can't wind up with one. Come on, I had some laughs with Linda. Yeah with Linda 'cause there's no pressure with Linda; I'm not tryin' to make her. I'm sure if I met her on a date we wouldn't have any fun at all. It's the girls I try and score with that I can't get to first base with.

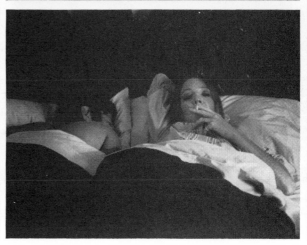

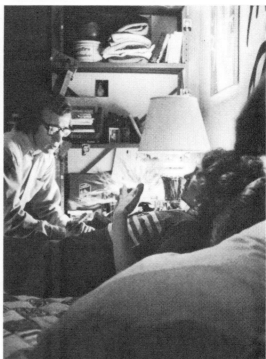

Allan: I'm turning into the Strike-Out King of San Francisco.

Nancy: Allan, what do you expect? Didn't I always say you're not the romantic type?

Allan: What's the matter with me, Nancy?

Nancy: You're a dreamer—you're awkward, you're clumsy. They can see how desperate you are. You know this; you said it yourself.

Allan: Don't go by that girl tonight; she was nothin'; I was toying with her.

Nancy: Oh face it, Allan. You may be very sweet but you're not sexy.

Allan: Well don't be so sure. You never said that when we were married.

Nancy: I was thinkin' it.

Allan: Bet she *was*. I wonder if she actually had an orgasm in the two years we were married or—did she fake it that night.

Allan: Hello, is this the Perry residence? Umm can I speak to Marilyn? Umm Allan Felix, an old friend of hers from Midwood High School; I dated her once.

Allan—Do you remember? I'm stunned; it was eleven years ago. That's right. Right. Short, with red hair and glasses. Yes. No no no tha-that's cleared up. Well . . . we-how-how can I get in touch with her? Oh really?—

Allan—She still feels that way? Well it's been eleven years. When did you last speak with 'er? Yeah? Last week, uh?—

Allan—And she specified that uh—she didn't want you to give me the number? I see. Okay, thank you. Yes. Okay.

Linda: Excuse me uh—could you tell me where Mister Felix is?
Girl: Sure, right through that door; he's in the projection room.
Linda: Oh, okay. Thank you.

Linda: Allan? Are you busy?
Allan: What're you doing here?

Linda: Uhhh I don't feel so hot.
Allan: What's the matter?
Linda: What do you have for an anxiety attack? I need a tranquilizer.

Allan: I got everything; I'm a drug store. What's wrong?
Linda: I have this throbbing in the pit of my stomach.
Allan: Yeah? Well how do you know it's anxiety? How do you know it's not—fear?

Linda: My stomach feels jumpy.
Allan: Do you actually find it hard to breathe?
Linda: Yeah, a little. I feel frightened and I don't know what over.

Allan: Yeah, I get that.
Linda: What is it—fear or anxiety?
Allan: Homosexual panic.

Linda: Ohhh. You know I always get this way when Dick goes on a business trip.
Allan: Oh?

Linda: Yeah he had to fly to Cleveland for the day. I got up, helped him pack, drove him to the airport and threw up in the United Airlines terminal.

Allan: Yeah it's a good terminal; I've thrown up there.
Linda: You know I don't know what it is that upsets me so.
Allan: It's fear of separation.
Linda: Really?

Allan: It's an interesting psychological phenomenon. I hadda go to Washington once when I was married, and even though I was the one leaving I got sick. Y'know when I returned my wife threw up.

Linda: Well my analyst would say that I'm feeling guilty because I really want 'im to go.
Allan: That's funny. I cannot understand you. You know you're such a knockout; why're you such a mass of symptoms?
Linda: Why is anybody screwed up?

Linda: I guess it happens to you when you're a child. You know, you think you're ugly and your parents get divorced; you feel abandoned. You must have the same sort of thing.

Allan: No, my parents never got divorced. Although I begged them to.

Linda: I know you think I'm real nice, Allan, and I appreciate it. It's good for my ego.

Allan: Yeah I do and I'm hypercritical you know; it's part of my sickness; I—have a tendency to reject before I get rejected. Uh that way I save a lot of time and money.

Linda: Hey, no date tonight?

Allan: Yeah I had a date with a girl but she called it off—some kind of Polish holiday.

Linda: Oh. Well, why don't we go out to dinner and maybe hit a movie?

Allan: Okay. I have a better idea, why don't we have dinner at my house because the Late Show is showing *The Big Sleep* tonight.

Linda: Okay, do we have anything at your house for me to cook or should we go over to mine?

Allan: No, I have, I have frozen steaks and a bottle of champagne left.

Linda: What're you doing with champagne? you going to launch a ship?

Allan: No I tried to cook home last week to impress a girl. I tried to make Beef Stroganoff in the pressure cooker.

Linda: How'd it taste?

Allan: I don't know; it's still on the wall.

Linda: Okay, well listen, I'll buy some stuff and I'll bring it over to your house and fix it.

Allan: That'll be fabulous.

Linda: Okay, lessee, I'll get some asparagus and some salad and dessert. Y'know I-I love to cook but I never get a chance 'cause Dick's so busy all the time.

Allan: That'll be great. Get a whole lot o' stuff, you know.

Linda: You can open the champagne but not if I'm the only one that's going to drink it.

Allan: No. I'll have one or two with you but you have to promise to put me to bed if I dance naked.

Allan: Boy, it's gonna be great. I got a terrific rapport with Linda. I hate to see her depressed. It'll be real nice, nice cozy evening in—build a little fire . . .

Allan—Oh I'll . . . get some candles at the store, set up some atmosphere.

Allan—I can open a bottle of champagne.

Allan—Women are such suckers for champagne; it makes 'em cra—zy.

Allan—Makes 'em crazy? Hey wait a minute, what th' hell am I talking about here? This is Linda, Dick's wife.

Bogart: So, you finally fell in love with 'er, eh?
Allan: No, I just got carried away for a minute.

Bogart: Come on, kid; you don't have to feel guilty.
Allan: Guilty over what? Two lonely people with a tremendous amount in common have dinner together. We're Platonic friends.

Bogart: Now there's nothing Platonic about the way she thinks of *you*.
Allan: Yeah? how can you tell?

Bogart: Whaddaya want 'er to do? attack you? Don't get those candles; those are for a Jewish holiday; get romantic candles.

Allan: Well she's my friend's wife!

Nancy: Of course she is. She'll tell Dick and he'll beat you to a pulp.

Bogart:
Look, she loves
you, not him.

Nancy:
He's not the
romantic type.
Bogart:
Well he could
be if he tried.
Nancy:
Don't listen to
him.
Bogart:
Don't listen to
her!

Allan:
Fellas, we're in a
supermarket!

Allan: Get a grip on yourself, she's married. And to your best friend. Aw they're never gonna get a divorce either. Huh! Why can't I ever get a break?

Dick: Allan, I'd like you to do me a favor.
Allan: Yes?

Dick: I've fallen in love with another woman. Don't ask me how, it just happened. We're going off together to live in Alaska. She's an Eskimo. I know you and Linda've always been fond of one another and I thought perhaps while I'm gone you'll look after her. It would mean a lot to me.
Allan: Of course.

Dick: Well I'm off to Alaska. If you need me I'll be at Frozen Tundra six, nine two nine oh.

Allan: I'm so tense. I don't know what's wrong. She'll be here any second.

Allan—She *is* always complimenting me. I *know* she likes me. But does she like me—that way.

Allan—What th' hell, I could—I could—test 'er.

Allan: I could make an advance . . .
What could possibly go wrong.

Allan: Linda, my darling!
Linda: Allan, don't!

Allan: It was meant to be.
Linda: Allan, take your hands off me; you must be crazy!

Allan: Linda, my love!
Linda: Allan—I'm a married woman. Rape!!

Allan: Look—let's not get carried away.

Allan—I'm not an appealing guy.

Allan—The thought that a girl like Linda could fall for me—

Allan—I'm kidding myself.

Allan: Where the hell is she anyhow?

Allan—By now she coulda had her goddamn steak and been outa here.

DING DONG

Linda: Oh I feel so light, that Librium I took today is really beginning to work.

Allan: Well look, maybe you better not have any champagne.

Linda: Oh no, what the hell, if I get a little carried away you can always call the police.

Allan: How long did you say Dick was gonna be out of town for?

Linda: Ah he'll be back tomorrow.

Allan: There's a new Truffaut film at the Regency, I think maybe we should go out and see it.
Linda: Oh come on, you're kidding. We're all set for here and besides it's starting to rain and I just remembered that great Ida Lupino movie's on Channel Four.

Linda—You know the one where she's happily married and suddenly becomes involved with her husband's best friend.
Allan: How does it end?

Linda: She kills them and herself.
Allan: Let's go out.
Linda: Oh no, Allan; I really want to see that Ida Lupino movie; it's a fascinating theme.

Linda—Do you think it's possible to love two people at once?
Allan: What do you mean?

Linda: Well, a wife happily married suddenly finds out she loves another man. Not that she doesn't love her husband, just that she loves somebody else. Do you think that's very possible?
Allan: Do you?

Linda: Oh very. Very possible and probably very common. Love is such a strange phenomenon. Strange and exquisite.

Bogart: Go ahead. Make your move.

Allan: No, I can't.

Bogart: Go ahead; take her and kiss her.

Linda: Is anything wrong, Allan?

Bogart: Go ahead, she wants it.

Allan: No, I don't want to.

Linda: Yes?

Bogart: Hurry, before she moves out of position.

Bogart—Kiss 'er kid. Go on!

Bogart: Well, kid—you blew it.

Linda: I guess I better begin our potatoes.

Allan: How does it look? I invite 'er over and then come on like a sex degenerate. What am I, a rapist?
Bogart: You're getting carried away. You *think* too much. Just *do* it.

Allan: We're Platonic friends. I can't spoil that by coming on; she'll slap my face.

Bogart: Oh I've had my face slapped plenty o' times.

Allan: Yeah but your glasses don't go flying across the room.

Bogart: You're gonna disappoint 'er, kid.
Allan: I can't.

Linda: Here we are. Here, you can start on this.

Linda: Hey, did you read in the papers another Oakland woman was raped?
Allan: I was nowhere *near* Oakland!

Linda: Oh.

Allan: Do they know who did it?

Linda: Mmm, well they haven't a clue; he must be very clever.

Allan: Yeah you gotta have something on the ball to rape so many women and get away with it.

Linda: You know I think if anybody ever tried to rape me I'd just pretend to go along with it until the middle and then—

Linda—grab hold of the nearest heavy object and let 'im have it.

Linda: That is, unless of course I was enjoying it.

Allan: They say it's the secret desire of every woman.

Linda: I guess that depends on who's doing the raping.

Allan: Well, why dwell on morbid subjects. I'll tell you you'll never get raped.

Linda: No, not with my luck.

Linda: Oh I feel so light. That drink is going right to my head, I'm floating.

Bogart: Go ahead, kiss 'er.
Allan: I can't.
Bogart: She's ready.
Allan: How can you be sure?

Bogart: Believe me, I'm sure.
Allan: She'll pull back. I can feel it.

Bogart: Look, she's waiting and waiting; now don't screw up.

Allan: All right, I'm gonna try but I'm gonna go slow. If she screams I'll pretend it was a joke.

Bogart: Hurry up.

Allan: She better laugh.

Allan: Oh!

Allan—The phone! Oh!

Allan: Hello? Dick? Yes, yes she's here. Yes, she came over before. I was going out, I had a Polish date. Sh . . . Yeah.

Allan—It's for you—it's from Cleveland, it's Dick. Yes, she's right . . .

Linda: Are you upset over anything?
Allan: No I was startled by the ring.

Allan: I want 'er out! I can't handle this; I'm gonna cause an international incident.
Linda: Hello, darling?

Allan: 'Hello darling', she loves him. What'm I kidding myself.

Bogart: Will you relax? You're as nervous as Lizabeth Scott was before I blew 'er brains out. Look, all you gotta do is make your move and you're home free.

Allan: Oh this is crazy; we're all gonna wind up on the front page of the National Enquirer.

Linda: Okay. Goodbye. Ye-yes. Yes I will.

Linda—Dick sounded a little down; I think he's having some trouble in Cleveland.

Allan: How come he never takes you with 'im when he goes on those outa-town trips?
Linda: No, I'm afraid to fly. My analyst says it's an excuse. He never asks me along though. Who knows, maybe he's got something going on the side.

Allan: And would that bother you?
Linda: Oh sure, I mean not if I didn't know.

Allan: So then it would hurt Dick a lot if you ever had uh—like a casual affair with anybody else?

Linda: Oh I don't think I could have a casual affair.
Allan: No?
Linda: No, I don't take those things lightly.

Linda—You know if I fell for another man there'd have to be something more there than just a fling. I mean I'd have to feel something more serious in which ca . . . are you shaking?
Allan: No, I'm chilly, just chilly.

Linda: Mmm. It's not very cold.

Linda—Anyway I'm—I'm not the type for an affair. I don't think I could take the excitement involved. Besides I'm not glamorous enough.
Allan: What do you mean? You're uncommonly beautiful.

Linda: Oh, when I go out with you and all those beautiful young girls, I feel as though—life has passed me by. I should be selling chocolates at Fanny Farmer.
Allan: Are you nuts? Those girls are not in your league.

Linda: Oh keep talking; you're saving my life. I have—such an inferiority complex.
Bogart: You're handling yourself very well. Now kiss 'er.

Allan: Pleeeease! Bogart: You built up to it beautifully.
Allan: I don't have the nerve.
Bogart: Look, tell 'er how beautiful she is again.
Allan: I just told 'er. Bogart: Again!

Allan: You really are—an unusually beautiful person.
Linda: Oh, Allan, I don't know what to say to that.

Allan: No, really, you're unus—you are exceptionally beautiful. You're—you're a very beautiful girl, you know?

Allan: You are very uncommonly beautiful. You're an unusually beautiful girl . . . an extreme. . . .

Bogart: All right already!

Linda: It's been so long since anybody said that to me.
Bogart: Now move closer to 'er.

Allan: How close?
Bogart: The length of your lips.

Allan: That's *very* close.
Bogart: Come on, move.

Allan: Now what?
Bogart: Now—tell 'er that she moves something in you that you can't control.
Allan: You're kidding!
Bogart: Go ahead.

Allan: From me it's corny.
Bogart: She'll love it.
Allan: It's like Fred Astaire looks great in tails; I look lousy.

Bogart: Will you leave Fred Astaire outa this!
Allan: . . . in that sort of situation . . .
Bogart: . . . and say something.

Allan: I love the time we've spent together.
Linda: So've I.

Allan: Is that awright? I don't wanta use your other line about moving something . . .
Bogart: You're doing fine, kid.

Bogart—Now—tell her she has the most irresistible eyes you've ever seen.

Allan: You have—the most—eyes I've ever seen on any person. Your eyes . . .

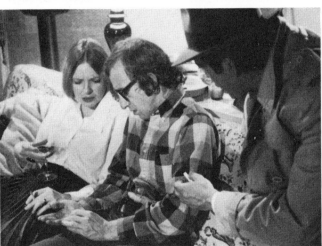

Linda: Allan, your hand is trembling.
Allan: It is?
Bogart: That's because you're near.

Allan: Pardon me?

Bogart: Tell 'er that!

Allan: That's because you're near.
Linda: Ohh—you really know what to say, don't you?

Bogart: Now—tell 'er that you've met a lot of dames but she is *really something special*.
Allan: Oh that she won't believe.

Bogart: Oh no?

Allan: I have met a lot of dames—but you are really—something—special.
Linda: Reeeally?

Allan: She bought it!

Bogart: Okay. Now put your right hand around her shoulders and pull her close . . .

Allan: That I can't do. No. I really . . .
Bogart: Go on!

Allan: I'll try.

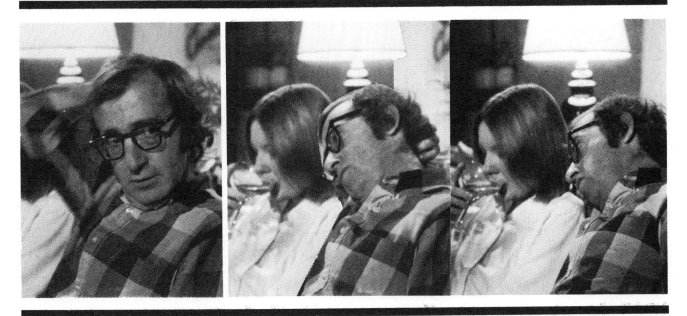

Linda: Ohhh . . .
Bogart: Now. Get ready for the big move and do exactly as I tell you.

Nancy: I warned you to leave my ex-husband alone!

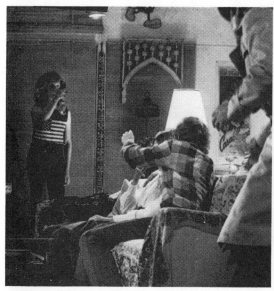
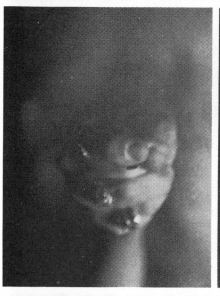

Linda: Well—I guess I better fix the steaks.

Allan: Linda . . .
Linda: Huh?
Allan: You eyes—are like—two *thick steaks*!

CRASH!

Linda: Allan, don't!   Allan, I'll pay for the lamp.

Allan: It's all right, I think I love you.
Linda: No no, I insist on paying for the lamp.

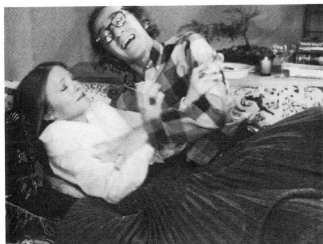 

Allan: Will you forget the lamp.
Linda: I'm so clumsy, Allan; will ya please take ten dollars?

Allan: Will ya forget the damn lamp! Gimme five dollars; we'll call it even.
Linda: Allan! Don't!

Allan: Linda, you're makin' a mistake. I was joking.

Allan: Linda, I was just testing you. It was not a technical kiss, it was a Platonic kiss.

Linda: Allan, I think I better go home.

Allan: You-you-you're making an e-enormous mistake!
Linda: No no, I really . . .
Allan: . . . to think that I would—that idea would occur to . . . Linda!

Linda: Please now I'll be crying . . .
Allan: Linda, you're getting the wrong idea.

Allan: I attacked 'er. I'm a vicious jungle beast. She's panicky. By the time she gets home she'll be hysterical. Oh what am I gonna tell Dick? She'll probably go right to police headquarters.

Allan—Oh what'd I do? I'm not Bogart, I never will be Bogart. I'm a disgrace to my sex.

Allan—I should get a job in an Arabian palace as a eunuch.

Allan—That's the Vice Squad!

Linda: Allan . . .
Allan: Linda.
Linda: Allan, did you say you love me?

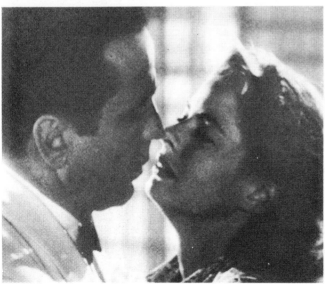

Linda: I still can't believe it.
Allan: I haven't slept that well in years. Is it noon yet?
Linda: No—it's seven.

Allan: Seven? I didn't realize it was so early. You were fantastic last night in bed.
Linda: Oh thanks.
Allan: How do ya feel now?

Linda: I think the Pepto-Bismol helped. What were you thinking about while we were doing it? Hmm?
Allan: Willie Mays.

Linda: Do you always think of baseball players when you're making love?
Allan: It keeps me going.

Linda: Yeah I couldn't figure out why you kept yelling 'Slide'.

Allan: Well . . . I guess it'd probably be best if *you* told Dick.
Linda: Well what'll I say?

Allan: If it happened, it happened, that's all. It's not your fault, it's not my fault. You felt like a woman last night and I felt like a man. And that's what those kind of people do.

Linda: But we can't sneak around and have an affair. I mean it's so cheap.

Allan: Well no, you know—gotta be honest with 'im—we—just have to tell 'im that uh—you know, th' two've you've grown apart and that—you and I've fallen in love. That's if you love me.

Linda: Oh I do, Allan.

Allan: Well then we have to tell 'im the truth.

Linda: I'm so tense.

Allan: Y'know maybe I'd better tell 'im. Y'know I-I think I've known 'im longer than you have.

Linda: No no, I prefer to do it.

Allan: Yeah, maybe you better do it.

Linda: Tell 'im what though?

Allan: Tell 'im that uh that the—two of us are right for each other and that uh—you know maybe you oughta think about—you know, getting your stuff out and moving out, maybe moving in with me for a while and give it a try, you know. Uh as long as I think as long as we handle this in a mature way uh—as long as *I'm* mature about it and you're mature about it and both of us are mature we—achieve a certain uhhh maturation which guarantees uh maturosity.

Linda: Yes, well, you're mature, Allan. And very wise.

Allan: Yes, well, well, I think the key to wiseness is maturiosity.

Linda: Why is it always so complicated?
Allan: Lean on me, baby. Lean on me.

Linda: Oh!

Allan: If you want me, I'll be home on the floor having an anxiety attack.
Linda: Okay.

Allan: Well, kid, she loves ya. Why not? I was dynamite in bed last night. Whssh! That lucky girl. I gave her my *best* moves.

Allan: Oh excuse me—umm—could I—I want to take a look at the music box in the window.

Allan—It was it was a nice brown sort of uh—small music box.

Nancy: Allan. Al—lan!

Allan: Nancy! What're you doin' here?
Nancy: I saw you walk in; I was calling you. Didn't you hear me call you?
Allan: No, I was I was . . .
Nancy: You didn't?
Allan: . . . you know thinking about some stuff.
Nancy: Still daydreaming. How are you?
Allan: Okay; how are you?
Nancy: I'm okay. I just got back from New York; I'm gonna move back there again.

Allan: Reeeally?
Nancy: Uh huh.
Allan: That so?
Nancy: Yeah. So what're you doing?
Allan: Oh you know the usual, I—go to the movies and I, you know, stare off into space.
Nancy: Yeah. Are you seeing someone?

Allan: Not act- no. Mmmm. Y'know I'm you know I mean I go out but not no, no—
Nancy: How're Dick and Linda?
Allan: Just fine. You know, just fine; I . . .
Nancy: What?
Allan: . . . I wouldn't know, I mean . . .
Nancy: Well at least you're in a lot better spirits than when I moved out.
Allan: I am 'cause you got me in a . . .
Nancy: Yeah.
Allan: . . . up day, I mean, you know I've been . . .

Proprietor: Is this the music box you wanted?
Allan: Uh . . .
Nancy: Pretty.

Allan: Yeah. I'm gonna keep my paper clips in something so I you know . . .

Nancy: Listen I have an appointment with the diet doctor. I'm gonna go.

Allan: Nancy, you don't, you don't seem overweight to me, I mean . . .
Nancy: Let's not have that argument again.

Allan: Right.
Nancy: Right. 'Bye.
Allan: So long. It was nice seeing you.

Nancy: Thanks. You too.

Allan: I was real cool. Why not? She never understood me. I'm complicated.

Allan—I think Linda understands that. Linda finds me exciting. What th' hell, Dick'll understand. Why not? Because of our social encounters, a little romance has developed. It's a very natural thing among sophisticated people.

Dick: You sent for me?
Allan: Oh yes. **Dick:** Good.
Allan: Drink? **Dick:** Quite.
Allan: Scotch? **Dick:** Fine.

Allan: Neat? **Dick:** Please.
Allan: Soda? **Dick:** Dash.
Allan: Linda and I are in love.
Dick: It's just as well.

Dick: I've come from my doctor; he's given me two months to live.
Allan: Good. Then you don't mind?
Dick: Not a bit.
Allan: Cheers. **Dick:** Cheers.

Allan: Dick and I've been through a lot together. He's my best friend. This is terrible.

Allan—This is gonna hurt him, I know it.

Dick: How could they? My wife and my best friend. I loved 'er. I loved *him*.

Dick—Why didn't I see it coming? Me, who had the foresight to buy Polaroid at eight and a half.

Allan: Dick is an emotional guy. He's liable to . . . God knows what, kill himself, or something.

Allan: Kill *himself*? D'jever think of what he might do to you? You've heard of the unwritten law, you take a guy's wife, you humiliate 'im.

Allan—You've seen enough Italian movies. And Dick's got a temper.

Dick: Bastardo!

Dick: Pezzo di cornutu!

Dick: Tu mai tradutto me, eh?

Allan: No no ma non e vero!

Dick: Tu mi pigli per stupido, eh?

Allan: No, no me culpe mia!
Dick: Porco! Carogna!

Dick: Imbesi-le!

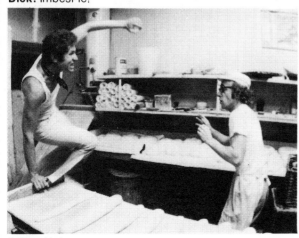

Allan: No!

Dick: Imbesile!

Allan: Ooh! Oooh! Mmmh! Mmmh!

Dick: Allan.

Allan: What're you doing here? You're supposed to be in Cleveland.

Dick: I had to come home. Allan, I gotta talk to you. I got a problem.

Allan: Well well whaddaya mean?
Dick: Allan—I think Linda's having an affair.

Dick: I called 'er at home; she's not there. These past few weeks she's been distant and distracted, little things only a husband would notice.

Dick—I don't understand it, Allan. You've seen her a lot these past few weeks; she's changed.

Dick—The other night she spoke about having an affair in her sleep.

Allan: Did she—mention any names?
Dick: Only yours. When I woke her and questioned her she said it was just a nightmare.

Dick: I keep tryin' to think of who it could be, Allan. It's gotta be somebody I don't know.

Dick: Somebody she met through work. An agent or a—an-an ad executive—a—photographer—uh—maybe an actor.
Allan: Don't get upset.

Dick: I love her, Allan. If she leaves me I'll kill myself.
Allan: Since when are you so emotional?

Dick: I've never been in love with anyone before in my whole life. If I find out who the guy is, Allan, I'll kill 'im, I swear!

Dick—I neglected her and now she's involved with some stud.

Dick—If I haven't already lost 'er to someone, Allan, I'm really gonna make up for everything to 'er.

Dick—I mean I'm gonna change. I'm gonna do everything I can to make her life with me fun and exciting,—

Dick—'cause without her it wouldn't be worth living. I was up all last night in a hotel room in Cleveland; I thought 'I—I'm losing her.

Dick—It's too bad; I'll survive.' Then I panicked and I called 'er. She was out.

Dick—When I called 'er here last night she said she was going straight home.

Dick—Where the hell did she stay?
Allan: Calm yourself.

Dick: I gotta find her, Allan. I've gotta stop her and beg her forgiveness before it's too late. I want 'er to get on that plane with me and go back to Cleveland.

Dick—I want 'er with me all the time. I want to hear her laugh and speak. I want to pamper her; I want to take care of her.

Dick—I'm sorry for carrying on like this, Allan, but you're the only friend in the world who would understand.

Allan: I understand.
Dick: Look, Allan—if she, Allan—Allan, if she calls, will you tell 'er I got I got to talk to 'er?

Dick—Tell 'er I'll see her at home, will ya?   **Dick**—Thanks a lot!

Allan: I'm gonna break up his home. He's crazy about 'er. I never realized how much. *He* never realized how much.

RINNGG!

RINNGG!

Linda: Yes?
Allan: Hello, Linda? Li . . . hello?

Allan—Lin . . . Ohhh! Sh. . . .

Linda: I'm in the middle of a conversation right now; Allan, I'll call ya back.

Allan: Linda, don't . . .

Dick: So that's really it?

RINNGG!

Linda: Yes?
Allan: Hello, Linda? Linda, I have to speak to you. Linda, have ya told him anything yet?

Dick: Who is that? Is that him?
Linda: This is Allan.

Linda: Allan, I'll-I'll speak to you later.

Allan: Linda, don't hang up the phone! Oh—Lin . . . oh! oh!

Allan: Hello, Linda, listen. This is urgent, I—Linda—you sound terrible.

Man: 有甚麽事？

Allan: Oh, oh excuse me. You changed . . . uh—uh . . .

Dick: Just hope you know what you're doing.
Linda: Oh, Dick . . .

RING!

Linda—Oh . . .

Allan: Hello, Linda? Linda, Linda, can ya are ya is it all right? Is the coast clear? Can I speak? Linda?

Dick: I really oughta be in Cleveland; there's an important session going on.

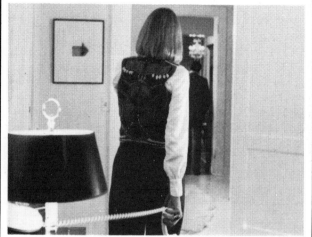

Linda: No, wait, Dick! Dick!
Allan: Say—just ans . . . Linda, just answer me if . . .

Linda: Oh look, I-I'll speak to you later, Allan.

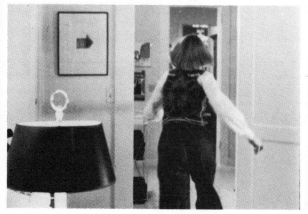

Allan: I don't believe this.

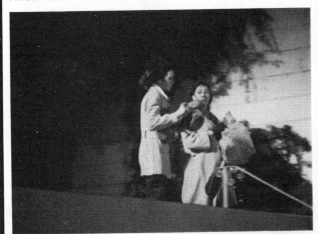

Linda: The airport.

Allan: . . . speak to 'er before she says anything to him.

Woman: If you're lookin' for the Christies, they just left for the airport.

Allan: Just now? together?
Woman: One right after the other.

Allan: Taxi!

Allan: I'll tell 'er it's over, that's all.

Allan—It was fun but uh—we—we lost our heads and—What if it's too late? What if Linda's *really* hooked on me? You know once a woman's been made love to by somebody who can *really* do it great . . . I was incredible last night in bed.

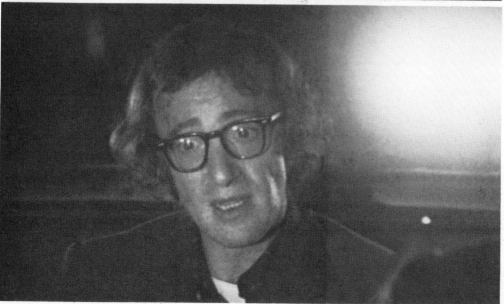

Allan—I never once had to sit up and consult the manual. Love is very different for a woman, it's a complicated phenomenon. And I don't know what to expect; I've never broken off with a girl before.

Linda: You told me you loved me.
Allan: Try to take it gracefully.
Linda: But the time we spent together, the closeness, the promises.
Allan: Linda, please . . .
Linda: You mean too much to me; I can't let you go.
Allan: Don't be difficult; I'm sorry.
Linda: Sorry's not enough; you think I'm some sort of play toy?

Allan: What can I say?
Linda: Give me the letter!
Allan: What letter?
Linda: Philip, give me the letter.
Allan: Linda, there is no letter.
Linda: I want the letter, Philip; give me the letter!
Allan: You're going crazy, Linda.
Linda: Don't treat me like this.
Allan: Don't pull the trigger, I'm a bleeder!

Bogart: Pull yourself together, kid; you're hysterical. You know you should feel encouraged. When you weren't coming on phony you got a pretty good dame to fall for ya. You never thought you could make it with dames, well you can.

Bogart: It's not that hard, kid. Watch.

Allan: But now it's gotta end and I don't know how to do it.

Bogart: Come 'ere, sweetheart.
Linda: Yes, darling?

Bogart: It's over.
Linda: What is?
Bogart: Us.
Linda: Over?
Bogart: That's right, toots. Over, kaput.

Linda: That simple, eh?
Bogart: That's right.
Linda: But supposing I say no?
Bogart: Won't do you any good.
Linda: Then will this?

Bogart: Now come off it, sugar; you never could use a rod.

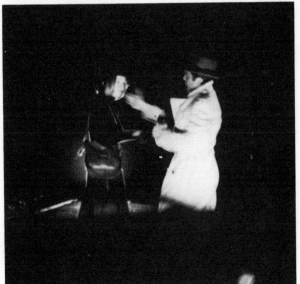

Linda: Uhh!

Linda: But why does it have to end before it can begin?

173

Bogart: Because you play too rough for me, sugar. It was *you* that killed Johnson. Parker found out about it so you killed him too but that wasn't good enough for you —

Bogart—ya wanted to finish me off. You knew you couldn't do it while I was facing you so you figured you'd get me to turn my back. But not me, sugar. Now let's go.

Bogart—You're taking the fall.

Bogart: That's all there is to it.

Allan: For you because you're Bogart.

Bogart—Listen, kid—there's other things in life besides dames, and one of 'em is to know you did a right thing for a pal. Think it over.

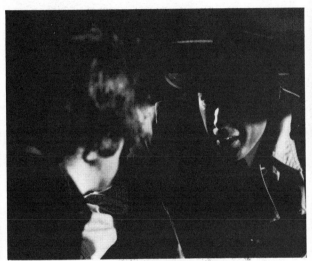

Bogart: Everybody is, kid, at certain times. You're doing something now I didn't think you had in ya. You're passin' up a real tomato because you don't wanta hurt a guy. If I did that there wouldn't be a dry eye in the house.

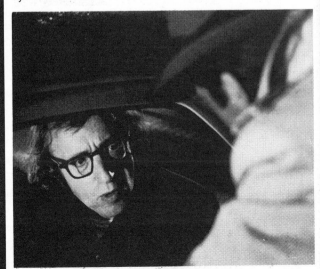

Allan: Yeah but I'm heartbroken over it.
Bogart: Well, all the more reason you should feel proud of it.
Allan: You think so?
Bogart: Sure.

Linda: Can you tell me what gate the flight to Cleveland is on?
Clerk: Yes. Gate fifteen.

Allan: Where does the plane to Cleveland take off?
Clerk: Gate fifteen.

Allan: Linda. Linda!

Allan: Linda! Linda! Wait . . .

Linda: Allan, what're you doing here?
Allan: Linda, I have something very important to tell you.

Linda: So do I.
Allan: Linda . . .

Linda: Allan, do you realize what a wonderful thing has happened? Allan, the most beautiful thing in the world has happened right under our very noses. We've had a wonderful experience. Doesn't that surprise you? You didn't have to do anything. You didn't have to leave any half-open books lying around—

Linda—you didn't have to have on the proper mood music —

Linda—why—I even saw you in your underwear with the days of the week written on them.

Allan: Linda, we have to call it quits.

Linda: Yes, I know.

Allan: Pardon me?

Linda: Suddenly everything became very clear.

Linda—And when I asked myself, do I really wanta break off my marriage? The answer is no. I love Dick.

Linda—And although somebody as wonderful as you is very tempting, I can't imagine my life without 'im.
Allan: You can't?

Linda: He needs me, Allan. And in some unexplainable way, I need him.

Allan: I know he needs you.

Linda: This's the first time I've ever been affected by anyone besides Dick.

Linda—I'm already in love with you.

Linda—Unless I stop it now I'll become too deeply involved to be able to go back to 'im.

Allan—If that plane leaves the ground and you're not on it with 'im, you'll regret it.

Linda—Oh, I don't regret a moment of what's happened because—what it's done for me is to reaffirm—my feelings for Dick.

Allan: Linda, I understand, really.
Linda: Are you sure? You're not just saying that to make things easy?

Allan—Maybe not today, maybe not tomorrow,—

Allan: No, I'm saying it because it's true. Inside of us we both know you belong to Dick; you're part of his work, the thing that keeps him going.

Allan—but soon and for the rest of your life.

181

Linda: That's beautiful.

Allan: It's from *Casablanca*.

Allan—I waited my whole life to say it.

Dick: I thought I saw you here.

Dick—What's going on?
Allan: There's something you should know before you two leave.

Dick: Us? You're coming with me?

Dick—Look—nobody owes me any explanations.

Allan: I'm going to anyhow because it may mean something to you later on.

183

Allan: You thought Linda was having an affair.
Dick: Yes.

Allan: What you didn't know was that she was at *my* house last night when you called.

Linda: Yes.

Allan—She came over to baby sit with me because I was lonely.

Allan: Over the past weeks I've fallen in love with 'er. I hoped she felt the same way —

Allan—Isn't that right, Linda?

Allan—I—I tried everything but—all she could talk about was you.

Dick: I understand.

Allan: I hope you do.

Dick: We better be going.

Dick: I'll call you, Allan.

Bogart: Well, I guess you won't be needing me any more. There's nothing I can tell you now that you don't already know.

Bogart: That was great. You've uh—you've really developed yourself a little style.

Allan: I guess that's so. I guess the secret's not being you it's being me.

Allan: Yeah. I do have a certain amount of style, don't I?

Allan—True, you're—you're not too tall and kinda ugly but—

Allan—what th' hell, I'm short enough and ugly enough to succeed on my own.
Bogart: Hmmm.

Bogart:
Here's looking at *you*, kid.

director of photography
OWEN ROIZMAN

music
BILLY GOLDENBERG

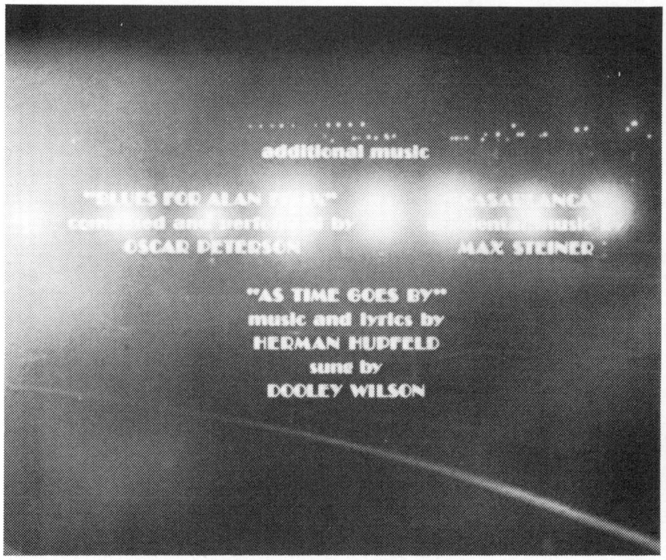

additional music

"BLUES FOR ALAN FELIX"
composed and performed by
OSCAR PETERSON

CASABLANCA
original music
MAX STEINER

"AS TIME GOES BY"
music and lyrics by
HERMAN HUPFELD
sung by
DOOLEY WILSON

film editor
MARION ROTHMAN

production designer
ED WITTSTEIN

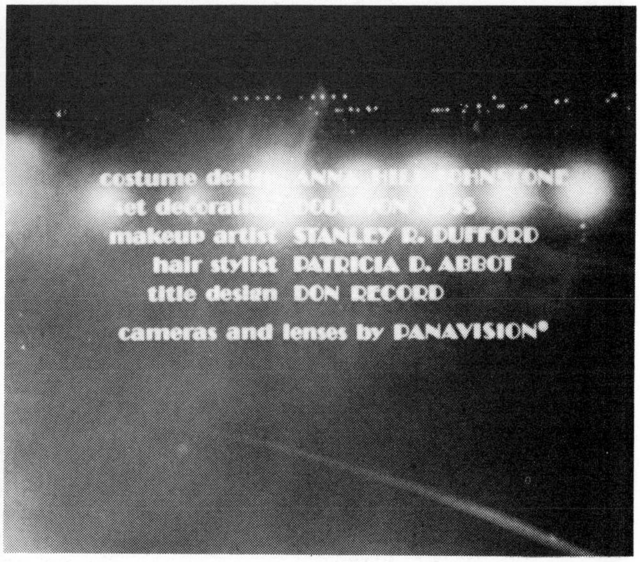

costume design ANNA HILL JOHNSTONE
set decoration ROBERT DRUMHELLER
makeup artist STANLEY R. DUFFORD
hair stylist PATRICIA D. ABBOT
title design DON RECORD

cameras and lenses by PANAVISION®

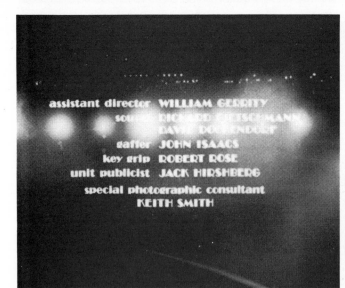

assistant director WILLIAM GERRITY
sound RICHARD GIETSCHMANN
DAVID DOCKENDORF
gaffer JOHN ISAACS
key grip ROBERT ROSE
unit publicist JACK HIRSHBERG
special photographic consultant
KEITH SMITH

AN APJAC PICTURE   color by TECHNICOLOR

THE PERSONS AND EVENTS IN THE PICTURE
ARE FICTIONAL. ANY SIMILARITY TO ACTUAL
PERSONS AND EVENTS IS UNINTENTIONAL.

COPYRIGHT ©1972 BY PARAMOUNT PICTURES CORPORATION. ALL RIGHTS RESERVED.
Paramount Pictures Corporation

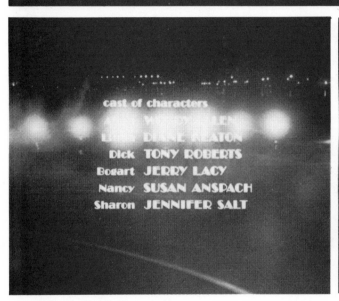

cast of characters
Allan WOODY ALLEN
Linda DIANE KEATON
Dick TONY ROBERTS
Bogart JERRY LACY
Nancy SUSAN ANSPACH
Sharon JENNIFER SALT

Julie JOY BANG
Jennifer VIVA
Discotheque Girl SUZANNE ZENOR
Museum Girl DIANA DAVILA
Fantasy Sharon MARI FLETCHER
Hood #1 MICHAEL GREENE
Hood #2 TED MARKLAND

Paramount
A Gulf+Western Company

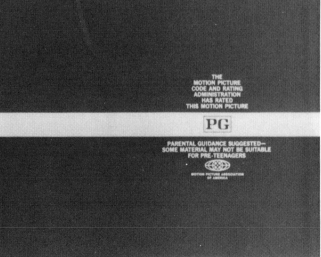

THE
MOTION PICTURE
CODE AND RATING
ADMINISTRATION
HAS RATED
THIS MOTION PICTURE

PG

PARENTAL GUIDANCE SUGGESTED—
SOME MATERIAL MAY NOT BE SUITABLE
FOR PRE-TEENAGERS

MOTION PICTURE ASSOCIATION
OF AMERICA